LEARNING TARGETS
for Numeracy

Number

Key Stage 1

Wendy Clemson
David Clemson

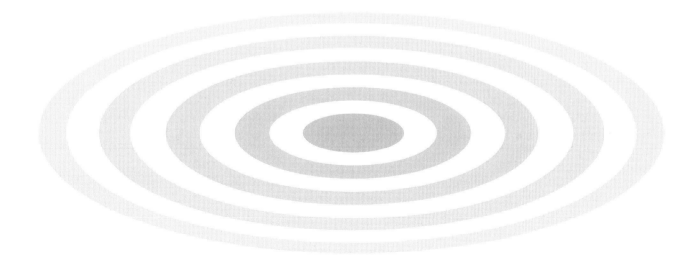

Stanley Thornes (Publishers) Ltd

Stanley Thornes for TEACHERS:
BLUEPRINTS • PRIMARY COLOURS • LEARNING TARGETS

Stanley Thornes for Teachers publishes practical teacher's ideas books and photocopiable resources for use in primary schools. Our three key series, **Blueprints**, **Primary Colours** and **Learning Targets** together provide busy teachers with unbeatable curriculum coverage, inspiration and value for money. We mail teachers and schools about our books regularly. To join the mailing list simply photocopy and complete the form below and return using the **FREEPOST** address to receive regular updates on our new and existing titles. You may also like to add the name of a friend who would be interested in being on the mailing list. Books can be bought by credit card over the telephone and information obtained on (01242) 267280.

Please add my name to the *Stanley Thornes for* TEACHERS mailing list.

Mr/Mrs/Miss/Ms _____

Address _____

_____ postcode _____

School address _____

_____ postcode _____

Please also send information about *Stanley Thornes for* TEACHERS to:

Mr/Mrs/Miss/Ms _____

Address _____

_____ postcode _____

To: Marketing Services Dept., Stanley Thornes Ltd, FREEPOST (GR 782), Cheltenham, GL50 1BR

First published in 1999 by
Stanley Thornes Publishers Ltd
Ellenborough House
Wellington Street
Cheltenham GL50 1YW

99 00 01 02 03 / 10 9 8 7 6 5 4 3 2 1

A catalogue record for this book is available from the British Library.

ISBN 0-7487-3590-9

Printed and bound in Great Britain by Redwood Books, Trowbridge, Wiltshire.

CONTENTS

Welcome to
LEARNING TARGETS

Learning Targets is a series of practical teacher's resource books written to help you to plan and deliver well-structured, professional lessons in line with all the relevant curriculum documents.

Each Learning Target book provides exceptionally clear lesson plans that cover the whole of its stated curriculum plus a large bank of carefully structured copymasters. Links to the key curriculum documents are provided throughout to enable you to plan effectively.

The Learning Targets series has been written in response to the challenge confronting teachers not just to come up with teaching ideas that cover the curriculum but to ensure that they deliver high quality lessons every lesson with the emphasis on raising standards of pupil achievement.

The recent thinking from OFSTED, and the National Literacy and Numeracy Strategies on the key factors in effective teaching has been built into the structure of Learning Targets. These might be briefly summarised as follows:

➤➤ that effective teaching is active teaching directed to very clear objectives
➤➤ that good lessons are delivered with pace, rigour and purpose
➤➤ that good teaching requires a range of strategies – including interactive whole class sessions
➤➤ that ongoing formative assessment is essential to plan children's learning
➤➤ that differentiation is necessary but that it must be realistic.

The emphasis in Learning Targets is on absolute clarity. We have written and designed the books to enable you to access and deliver effective lessons as easily as possible, with the following aims:

➤➤ to plan and deliver rigorous, well-structured lessons
➤➤ to set explicit targets for achievement in every lesson that you teach
➤➤ to make the children aware of what they are going to learn
➤➤ to put the emphasis on direct, active teaching every time
➤➤ to make effective use of time and resources
➤➤ to employ the full range of recommended strategies whole-class, group and individual work
➤➤ to differentiate for ability groups realistically
➤➤ to use ongoing formative assessment to plan your next step
➤➤ to have ready access to usable pupil copymasters to support your teaching.

The page opposite provides an at-a-glance guide to the key features of the Learning Targets lessons and explains how they will enable you deliver effective lessons. The key to symbols on the lesson plans is set out here. ➤➤

How to deliver structured lessons with pace, rigour and purpose

Explicit targets for achievement in every lesson

The concise subject knowledge you need

Crystal clear lesson plan layouts

The full range of teaching strategies

Rigorous and practical activities

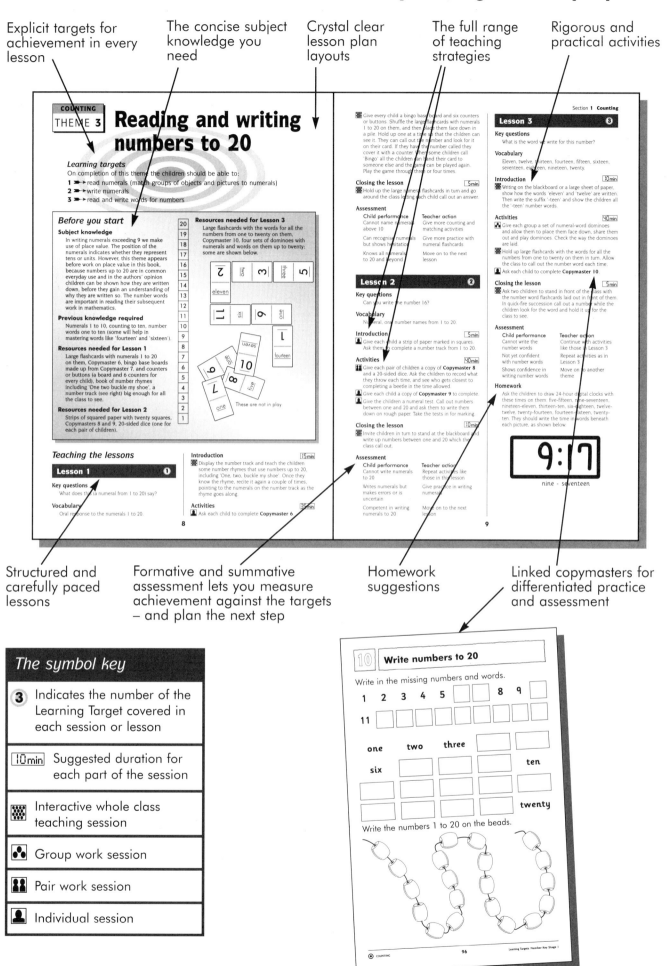

Structured and carefully paced lessons

Formative and summative assessment lets you measure achievement against the targets – and plan the next step

Homework suggestions

Linked copymasters for differentiated practice and assessment

The symbol key

(3) Indicates the number of the Learning Target covered in each session or lesson

10min Suggested duration for each part of the session

Interactive whole class teaching session

Group work session

Pair work session

Individual session

INTRODUCTION

Learning Targets: *Number Key Stage* 1 includes lessons on all of the main ideas in number for children aged 5–7 (Years R–2/P1–3). Together with its companion book *Learning Targets*: *Shape, Space and Measures Key Stage* 1, it offers support for the teaching of all the key features of mathematics suitable for children of this age group. In planning and writing this book the authors have not only sought to meet the requirements of the National Curriculum (England and Wales), and Curriculum and Assessment in Scotland: National Guidelines: Mathematics 5–14, but have also borne in mind the fact that there are currently demands for teachers to use direct and whole class teaching as a regular part of their teaching repertoire, and that teachers need to be aware of and address the imperatives highlighted in the National Numeracy Project.

This book and its companion volume do not, of course, constitute a complete scheme. They cannot provide you with all the resources needed for every mathematics session. As they cover all of the main ideas in mathematics work, however, these books are a backbone resource for mathematics teaching. There are some lessons at each level of work appropriate for the Key Stages. These texts can, therefore, be seen as an extremely valuable and effective aid to the delivery of directly taught lessons. They contain a series of well-structured, detailed and specific lesson plans, backed by linked Copymasters, which you can use to teach lessons in line with national curricula and the National Numeracy Project.

As each of the four mathematics books in the series addresses work at a whole Key Stage (either Years R–2/P1–3 or Years 3–6/P4–7), it is necessary to select lessons at the appropriate level. To help you do this, the books are organised into sections which each contain a number of themes. There is a progression from the start of each section to its end. Within each theme there are three lessons which also offer a progression, and the lessons should, therefore, be taught in order.

How this book is organised

Sections

This book is organised into six sections: Counting; Addition and Subtraction; Fractions; Multiplication and Division; Mental Arithmetic and Number Patterns; and Number Data. This last section concentrates on data collection and analysis in the context of number work.

At the start of each section you will find a short overview of the mathematics ideas which we see as important in offering the children appropriate learning opportunities. A section is divided into a number of themes, each with its own set of clear learning targets. There is a progression within each section. To conclude each section there is a set of extension ideas. These can be used in any mathematics session where the key ideas related to this section are being worked on. They may be incorporated within a programme of lessons, used in sessions that immediately follow learning target lessons, used in sessions designated as mathematical investigation sessions or used as additional homework activities.

Themes

The order of the themes within each section has been arranged to offer progression. Thus, in the Section 1: Counting, there are six themes. The first theme, 'Beginning counting', may be seen as more appropriate for children at an earlier stage in their mathematical education than, for example, the third theme 'Reading and writing numbers to 20'. Thus, 'Beginning counting' might be the theme tackled in Year R/P1, while the theme on reading and writing numbers to 20 may form part of the course for a Year 1/P2 class of children. The themes which follow place an increasing demand on children's mathematical skills and knowledge, and might therefore be taught to Top Infants (in Year 2/P3).

Within each theme, the lessons are also sequenced to provide more demand as the children move on from the first, to second and then third. The learning targets state explicitly what the children should know or be able to do by the end of each lesson. The learning targets provide you with a clear set of assessable objectives.

The themes in a section together form an overall set of lesson plans for a mathematics topic. The themes are free-standing. It is also possible for you to choose lessons from within a theme as free-standing lessons. At the end of each lesson there are descriptions of children's performance and suggested teacher actions. At the end of each theme there are suggestions for homework activities.

The lesson plans with each theme are very specific and detailed in their teaching suggestions, written to allow you to undertake direct teaching to clear objectives. Some lessons have accompanying Copymasters which are completely integrated into the teaching activities.

National Curricula and Numeracy

The lessons in this book have been written to meet the time demands of the 'numeracy hour' and the mathematical ideas match the required range of work in national curricula and those seen as important in the National Numeracy Project.

The need to revisit mathematics topics as children progress through Key Stage 1 (Year R–2/P1–3) has meant that the book is organised into sections which, as we have already indicated, can be used flexibly across the whole age range. We have written the lessons so that the teacher can differentiate between children's learning by the outcomes of their work.

Each theme can provide the material for a string of numeracy hours. Every teacher will interpret the demands of the numeracy hour in the light of their own situation and the structure of the book allows for this. To plan your number work we suggest that you consult the appropriate section and theme title to locate the lesson you want when you wish to offer a direct teaching session to your class.

The learning targets for each theme have been mapped against the Programmes of Study in the National Curriculum for England and Wales, Levels 1–3 and areas in the National Numeracy Project Recommendations. These charts are presented on pages viii–ix.

The learning targets for each theme have also been mapped against the statements in the attainment targets in Curriculum and Assessment in Scotland: National Guidelines: Mathematics 5–14 at Levels A and B. This chart is presented on page x. Teachers in Scotland can therefore be confident that the lessons in this book meet the requirements to which they are working.

Theme No.	Counting/Number properties	Place value/ordering	Estimating/Rounding	Fractions/Decimals	Understand + and −	Recall + and − facts	Mental strategies + and −	× and ÷	Recall × and ÷ facts	Mental strategies × and ÷	Checking	Making decisions	Reasoning about numbers	Problems 'real life'/money	Data handling	
1	●															
2	●	●														
3		●														
4		●														
5		●														
6		●														
7					●	●										
8	●	●			●	●	●				●					
9					●	●										
10					●	●	●									
11					●	●	●									
12			●		●	●	●									
13					●		●							●		
14				●												
15				●												
16	●	●		●												
17								●					●			
18								●	●	●						
19								●	●	●						
20								●								
21								●	●	●						
22								●	●	●						
23	●												●			
24					●	●	●									
25					●	●	●	●	●	●			●			
26												●		●		
27					●	●	●	●	●	●		●	●	●		
28															●	
29															●	

Curriculum planners
Programmes of study in the National Curriculum (England and Wales)

Number

Theme No.	2a	2b	2c	3a	3b	3c	3d	3e	4a	4b	4c	4d	5a	5b
1	•													
2	•	•												
3		•												
4		•												
5		•												
6		•												
7						•			•					
8	•	•				•			•					
9					•	•			•					
10						•								
11						•								
12		•					•		•					
13									•					
14			•											
15			•											
16	•	•	•											
17				•	•					•				
18						•								
19						•								
20										•				
21						•								
22										•				
23	•			•										
24					•	•	•		•					
25				•	•	•			•	•				
26										•				
27					•	•			•	•				
28													•	•
29														•

ix

Curriculum planners
Scottish guidelines planner

	LEVEL A	LEVEL B
INFORMATION HANDLING ATTAINMENT TARGET		
Collect	Obtain information from a picture, video, or story Collect information about selves	Obtain information from pictures, diagrams Theme 29 Conduct a class survey
Organise	Tallying Counting Themes 1, 2, 3 Sorting into specific sets Theme 28	Use a tally sheet Use a simple database
Display	Using real objects Theme 28 Using pictures Theme 28 Drawing simple diagrams Theme 28	Using labels, charts and diagrams Themes 28, 29 Constructing a bar graph, graduated in units
Interpret	From displays, locating and counting Theme 28	From displays asking specific questions Themes 28, 29
NUMBER, MONEY AND MEASUREMENT* ATTAINMENT TARGET		
Range and type of numbers	Whole numbers 0–20 Themes 1, 2, 3, 16 Halves Themes 14, 16	Whole numbers to 100 then 1000 Themes 5, 6 Quarters Themes 15, 16
Money	1p, 2p, 5p, 10p, 20p coins Theme 26	Coins up to £1 Theme 26
Add and subtract	Mentally 0–10 Themes 7, 8, 9, 10, 23, 24, 27 Money applications to 10p Themes 13, 26	Mentally 0–20 Themes 11, 23, 24, 27 2 digits – without calculator Themes 12, 27 2 digits added to or subtracted from 3 digits – with calculator Money applications to £1 Themes 13, 26
Multiply and divide		Mentally 2, 3, 4, 5, 10 Themes 17, 18, 19, 20, 21 Without calculator 2 digit numbers by 2, 3, 4, 5, 10 Themes 17, 21 With calculator for 2 digit numbers multiplied/divided by any digits Applications to £1 Theme 26
Round numbers		Round 2 digit whole numbers to nearest 10
Fractions, percentages and ratios		Find halves and quarters Themes 14, 15, 16
Patterns and sequences	Simple number sequences Themes 4, 23 Copy, continue simple patterns Theme 23	Even and odd numbers Theme 23 Whole number sequences Theme 23 More complex sequences
Functions and equations		Find missing numbers Theme 25

*For coverage of measurement see the companion book: *Learning Targets: Shape, Space and Measures Key Stage 1.*

COUNTING

Counting can be both easy and difficult. The rules are easy but the applications are many and various, so counting can be a complex activity. This is, in part, due to the fact that we use the same symbols, words and numbers for different purposes. For example, we use them to define the total number in a set, to indicate the number of steps along a line, or to show the order and sequence of objects or positions on the line.

Counting has its origins in pre-history when people needed to record their possessions. Counting and tallying are complementary activities, both being based on the matching of symbols to real objects. There are many stories and legends that involve counts and counting and these often indicate the links to the long-felt human need to count real objects. For example, stories abound in different parts of the UK where the hero has to match objects accurately, counting them at least twice, and getting the same cardinal number. This practical concern of ensuring that we have both completed a count and included all of the appropriate items in the count is a real one for you and the children. Try putting a set of real counters in a circle and counting them.

How do you know that you have not counted one twice? This leads us to start grouping objects as sub-sets of our total set, based on twos, fives and tens – no doubt because of our two hands: five fingers on one hand and ten fingers on both. Thus, counting on in tens, for example, is an important experience to which we need to lead children. Of course, in making decisions about grouping in this way, there is a whole set of activities that needs to be considered and utilized including sorting, matching and ordering. At the heart of counting is the set of things, and particularly one-to-one matching.

Even though children encounter apparently different uses of symbols in counting they must also know of the invariance – the conservation – of number. Being able to take different kinds, collections or arrays of objects and yet be able to state that there are the same number of each is vital to counting and the later development of addition, subtraction, multiplication and division. In this unit the children progress through sorting, matching and naming to ordering and comparing. They go on to start to manipulate counts by counting on, other than in ones.

Beginning counting

Learning targets

On completion of this theme the children should be able to:

1 ➡➡ count to five

2 ➡➡ use words like more and less and do matching activities

3 ➡➡ count to ten

Before you start

Subject knowledge

This is the foundation stone for children's lifelong association with numbers. It is, therefore, of vital importance that the children have a wide breadth of experience at this crucial point. The key ideas have to do with the oral words we use in the sequence called counting and the children should be allowed to count anything – fingers, toes, toys – that can be counted and have access to stories, songs and rhymes that offer the rhythm and repetition of counting. Note that the focus of this theme is not cardinal number – that is the size of a count – though the children will need to have a sense of cardinal number in order to work with the ideas and vocabulary in lessons 1 and 2.

The lessons have been set out to fit 45 minutes to one hour sessions, but if it fits the structure of the school day better to try an activity with only a group at a time, or to split the session in half, the activities are sufficiently discrete for this to be possible. For some activities additional adult help would be invaluable, as it would be possible to do an activity with most of the class, while a group works on something else under the supervision of another adult.

Previous knowledge required

'Life experience' of sorting, grouping and tidying away, such as setting a table and playing with toys; as well as the opportunity to listen to and learn counting rhymes and songs.

Resources needed for Lesson 1

In addition to the children themselves, many sets of objects for counting, including enough of the following for each child to have five (when required): beads, small toys, soft toys, pencils, crayons; bead strings, sorting trays; General Copymaster 86 (photocopied and stuck onto card so that the individual pictures can be cut out), Copymaster 1, books of nursery rhymes.

Resources needed for Lesson 2

Copymaster 2; small toys, pencils and other resources as in Lesson 1; play table with cloth and plastic crockery and cutlery; counting cards made up from several copies of Copymaster 86 as shown below:

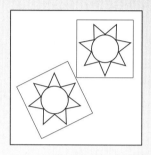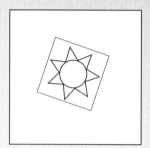
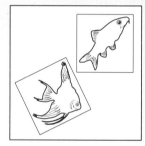

Resources needed for Lesson 3

Stories in which there is repetition and a string of characters appearing one at a time, for example, *The Enormous Pancake*, *The Elephant and the Bad Baby* (Vipont, E., Puffin, London, 1971), *The Troublesome Pig* (Lamont, P., Hamish Hamilton, London, 1983). Cuisenaire®, Unifix® or other similar maths apparatus. Picture cards made up in tens. Here are some suggested images for the picture cards. Make ten of each.

Teaching the lessons

Lesson 1 ①

Key questions

Can you count along?

What number comes next?

[handwritten: chn hold no. count order backward before/after]

Vocabulary

Count, one, two, three, four, five (oral only).

Introduction | 10 min |

Ask one child to stand in front of the others and allow the children to count along while you point to and count (for example) legs, eyes, ears, buttons, stripes, sleeves. Do the counting from left to right (from the children's point of view) as far as possible. Do the same activity using another child volunteer.

Activities | 35 min |

Set up a display on which there are things to count. While children look on, invite a child to point to the objects and do the counting. This display can be left on show for several days but should be changed each day. Here are example displays:

[handwritten: thread beads 5, 3 green, 2 blue etc]

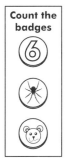
Count the badges
⑥

Come and count
Count the mugs

Count our holiday postcards

Using beads and a bead string, invite the child to do a variety of challenges involving, for example threading on the following: three of each colour; five of different colours; a one-two-one-two pattern. Or give the child some small toys, pencils or crayons to sort out using a sorting tray and then lay out five in a row. The counting or the sorts and arrays needs to be done with an adult looking on.

Begin work on some counting rhymes with the children. These can extend to five in this lesson. Examples include 'Five little speckled frogs', 'Five little ducks went swimming' (Withers, L., *Blueprints: Early Years Songs and Rhymes*, Stanley Thornes Publishers, Cheltenham, 1994). Counts can be done in other rhymes too, to show, for example, how many children went up the hill to fetch a pail of water or how many shoes my son John wore in bed.

Ask each child to complete **Copymaster 1**.

Closing the lesson | 10 min |

Use the card pictures made up from **Copymaster 86**. Place them in piles of fish, flowers, apples, socks, sheep, shells and ice creams. Give one fish card to each of five children. Ask them to stand in front of the class holding out their picture card. Allow all the children to count in unison along the row of pictures

[handwritten at bottom: Make count objects board + cards to match.]

from left to right. Repeat this activity with other picture sets.

Assessment

Child performance	Teacher action
Cannot say the numbers one to five while pointing to an array of objects	Give more practical and daily experience of counting, first to two and then to five. Use the counting display to give the chance for the children to count aloud
Can count to five in this way	Go on to the next lesson
Can count to five and beyond	Go on to the next lesson

Lesson 2 ②

Key questions

Which has more?

Is this group more or less than this group?

Can you match these?

[handwritten: chn stand up, 13 b how many, same, make same]

Vocabulary

More, less, fewer, the same, match.

Introduction | 5 min |

Ask two boys and two girls to stand in front of the other children. Put the girls together and the boys together. Ask 'Are there more girls than boys? Are there more boys than girls?' Set a boy alongside each girl and announce that there are the same number of boys as girls. Now ask four different girls and three different boys to stand in front of the class. Ask the questions again, and then set a boy alongside each girl. Announce that they are not 'the same'. 'There are more girls.' 'There is one more girl.'

Activities | 35 min |

Give each group five small toys and five other objects that go together, like card shapes or pencils. Call out instructions to the class and in their groups they should lay out the toys and other objects appropriately. Here are some suggested challenges.

- Set out the toys and give each a pencil to match. Ask 'How many toys?' 'How many pencils?' 'Are they the same?'

- Take two toys and four pencils. Lay the toys in a row. Match the pencils to the toys. Ask, 'Are there more toys or more pencils?'

- Take five toys and three pencils. Lay them out. Ask 'Are there fewer toys or fewer pencils?'

Note which children in each group are doing the work and pursue the tasks until every child has had a turn. For example say something like: 'The next challenge is for the girls; for the children with a baby brother; for the children with a white front door; for Alex, Malik, Nasseem and Tess.'

Ask the children to complete **Copymaster 2**.

While some children watch give others the chance to set the table for one, two, three, four or five of their friends or toys. They should be able to match a plate, a knife and so on to each place at the table.

Closing the lesson 10 min

Use cards with numbers of pictures on them as shown in the resources for this lesson. Hold up two at a time and ask 'Are they the same?' 'Are there more here or here?' 'Are there less here than here?'

Assessment

Child performance	Teacher action
Does not understand 'more', 'less' and 'the same'	Give more practice in comparing numbers of things in a whole range of everyday contexts
Can follow directions using 'more', 'less', 'the same' vocabulary	Move on to the next lesson
Follows directions and uses the vocabulary	Move on to the next lesson

Lesson 3 ③

Key questions

Can you count along?

What number comes next?

What comes after ... five, seven ...?

Vocabulary

Number words one to five, six, seven, eight, nine, ten (oral only).

Introduction 10 min

Invite ten children to stand in line at the front of the class. Starting at the left, from the children's point of view, ask the children to count along to five, and carry on counting, noting who is able to do so. Count several times more. Ask a child who is clearly confident at counting to act as teacher and do the pointing. Then for several more repetitions of the count invite different children to call the numbers out, for example all the children with cardigans, all

those having packed lunch today, or all those with black socks. Observe which children do not take part.

Activities 35 min

Give each pair of children small picture cards made up as shown in resources for this lesson. Allow the children to turn all the small cards face down. They take turns to flip them over and fill their arrays. They can then count and compare their arrays, which may look like the examples below.

Read a story, in which there is repetition and a string of characters appearing one at a time, and ask the children to count the characters.

Allow each child to draw a row of ten toys on a strip of paper. If you wish some can draw a 'shopping list' down the paper. Hold up some of the picture lists and allow all the children to count the items aloud.

Closing the lesson 10 min

Using Cuisenaire® ten-rods or Unifix® or similar apparatus, give one each to ten children. Count the ten children. Count the ten-rods. Then let each child place their rod on the teacher's desk or propped against the wall in turn. Count along with the children as they do this, until the row is complete.

Assessment

Child performance	Teacher action
Cannot count to ten	Recap counting to five, gradually increasing the number of objects
Counts to ten but not yet confident	Give more practice in counting to ten
Counts to ten with ease	Move on to the next lesson

Homework

Ask the children to make a picture frieze that they can use to count along. The pictures could be houses, cats, ducks, monsters or something of the children's own choosing. The children can also collect comics and cereal boxes which can be brought to school to make counting friezes of pictures of people from comics or favourite cereals.

Child 1

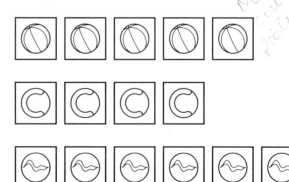

Child 2

THEME 2 Reading and writing numbers to 10

Learning targets

On completion of this theme the children should be able to:

1 ➤➤ record their counts by tallying and matching

2 ➤➤ read and write numerals

3 ➤➤ read and write words for numbers

Before you start

Subject knowledge

Symbols for numbers are a new language to children, for they are 'squiggles' to which we respond by saying words, and the words for numbers need to be learned in just the way that children learn to read other words. They should be shown the words in a range of contexts, told what the words 'say' and then have sight of each word many many times.

In our counting system there are only ten symbols to be learned, and these individual symbols or combinations of them allow us to write any number we like. These ten symbols are what make mathematics distinctive as a subject. However, there is a real danger that children fail to grasp the fact that the symbols are 'abstract' – that is, flexible and versatile – and begin to feel they have a meaning of their own. The symbol '2' has no meaning alone, it needs to be attached to or represent two objects – cats, dogs, toys, badges, sweets, etc.

The example number for Lesson 2 is three. The lesson can be adapted and repeated for other numbers exceeding three, up to ten. The example number for Lesson 3 is six. The children should have worked on the number words one to five before this lesson. The lesson can be adapted and repeated for numbers exceeding six.

Previous knowledge required

Sorting out, matching, counting to ten and the vocabulary to compare numbers of objects (more, less, the same, etc.)

Resources needed for Lesson 1

Toys and objects to use for counts (ten for each child); construction toys like Lego®, Lasy®; rough paper; Copymaster 3.

Resources needed for Lesson 2

(The example number for this lesson is three. The lesson can be adapted and repeated for other numbers exceeding three, up to ten.) Large flashcards with the numerals 1, 2 and 3 on them; toys and objects to use for counts (three for each child); spinners with the numerals 1, 2, 3, 1, 2, 3 on them (these can be made up using General Copymaster 50); counting apparatus like Unifix® and Centicubes®; Copymaster 4; track games and counters. There is a sample track game on Copymaster 88.

Resources needed for Lesson 3

(The example number for this lesson is six. The lesson can be adapted and repeated for numbers exceeding six.) Large flashcards each with a word for a number on it – 'one', 'two', 'three', 'four', 'five' and 'six' (enough for one for each child); large floor dice; Copymaster 5.

Teaching the lessons

Lesson 1 ①

Key questions

Can you make a picture of the toys and how you counted them?

Can you make a line on the paper to show each toy?

Vocabulary

Record, write, tally.

Introduction ⏱10 min

▦ Show the children two small sets of objects and show them how the objects can be 'matched' by setting them alongside one another. Draw the sets on the blackboard and put in lines to show how the match can be recorded. Take a fresh set of things and set them down on a piece of paper. Show how a tally mark can be made to show each object. Take the objects away and point to the marks to show how these can be counted as shown here.

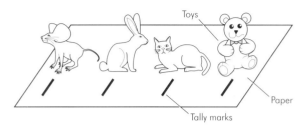

Activities [40 min]

👤 Ask the children to complete **Copymaster 3**. Then give each child up to ten toys and objects to use for counts to make their own tallies on rough paper.

👥 Give each work group some construction apparatus like Lego® or Lasy®. Ask them each to make a model with up to 10 pieces. They should then draw each piece on the rough paper and make a tally mark for each piece.

▦ Use a crate of games equipment (for example, skipping ropes, bats, balls, hoops). In a large space ask three children to sit in a row. Then invite a child at a time to set down, in front of each of the three children settled in the row, a skipping rope each. Ask another child to 'Give each person a bat'… then a ball and so on. The children can then chant the counts for the children, skipping ropes, bats, balls and so on. The children should also note that this way everyone gets one each.

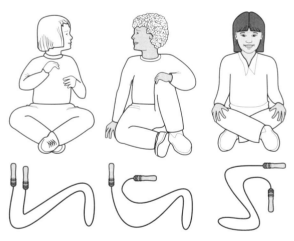

Children and equipment one-to-one

Closing the lesson [5 min]

▦ Draw outline sets of shapes on the board and invite a child to match the items or draw tally lines while the rest of the class look on.

Assessment

Child performance	Teacher action
Cannot match or tally	Return to work like that in Theme 1
Can match and tally but is tentative	Give more practice in matching and tallying
Shows confidence in matching and tallying	Move on to the next lesson

Lesson 2 ②

Key questions

What does this say?

How do we write the number three?

Vocabulary

Number, numeral, one, two, three.

Introduction [10 min]

▦ Show the children the flashcard with the numeral 1 on it. Ask what it says and invite the children to 'draw' their own 1 in the air. Show them how to start at the top of the 1 and draw down. Then show them the numeral 2 and then 3 repeating the actions.

Activities [35 min]

👥 Give each group toys and objects to use for counts; include three of each. They also need a set of cards with the numerals 1, 2 and 3 on them. Ask the children to set out groups of objects on their table and put by each group the number card to match. View what the children have done and ask each group to collect the objects together and then let each person have a turn at setting out. Inspect the results each time.

👤 Allow each child to complete **Copymaster 4**.

👥👥 Ask the children to play track games with spinners with the numerals 1, 2, 3, 1, 2, 3 on them, and two counters for each pair. Ask the children to spin the spinner and complete the track game. They can play it twice if there is time.

Closing the lesson [10 min]

▦ Hold up the numeral flashcards randomly and ask the children to do an action to show how many (for example clapping or stamping, or saying 'Hurrah!')

Assessment

Child performance	Teacher action
Does not recognise or write the numeral 3	Repeat the lesson giving practical matching, tracing and drawing activities
Uses 3 but lacks confidence or makes errors	Give more practical work and another chance at completing the Copymaster
Reads and writes the numeral 3	Move on to the next lesson

Lesson 3 ③

Key questions

What does this word say?

Can you write the word six?

Vocabulary

Number, word, one, two, three, four, five, six.

Introduction [10 min]

▦ Draw a large dot on the blackboard. Ask the children

how many dots there are and write the numeral and word alongside the dot. Continue these actions through the numbers up to six. Ask the children to close their eyes and 'see' the word for six. Ask several children in turn to come and write the word for six on the blackboard.

Activities
40 min

Ask the children to sit in a large circle. Give each child a large flashcard with a word for a number on it (there should be several of each with one, two, three, four, five or six on them). Toss the floor dice into the circle and ask the children with the word for the number thrown to show their flashcard. Everyone can then say the number. Ask a child near the dice to throw again. Repeat this activity many times.

Ask each child to complete **Copymaster 5**.

Using counting apparatus like Unifix® or Centicubes® the group can make towers of one, two, three, four, five and six blocks. These can be placed on a sheet of rough paper and the children should write in the number words to match.

Closing the lesson
10 min

Invite different children to draw giant letters on the blackboard or in felt tip on a large sheet of paper or in playground chalk on the playground, to show the word 'six'.

Assessment

Child performance	Teacher action
Cannot read or write six	Do more practical work involving six, and allow the children to trace the word and write 'six' in sand and join dots to make 'six' before tackling the Copymaster again
Can recognise six but not write it	Give practice in writing the word 'six' and then ask the child to repeat the Copymaster
Can read and write six	Move on to number words above six and then to another theme

Homework

The children can take home a track game and a spinner with the number words one to six on and play the game at home. Ask the children to look at a set of dominoes and draw all the dominoes that have six dots altogether on one half.

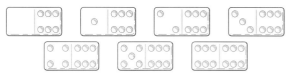

THEME 3 Reading and writing numbers to 20

Learning targets

On completion of this theme the children should be able to:

1 ➡➡ read numerals (match groups of objects and pictures to numerals)

2 ➡➡ write numerals

3 ➡➡ read and write words for numbers

Before you start

Subject knowledge

In writing numerals exceeding 9 we make use of place value. The position of the numerals indicates whether they represent tens or units. However, this theme appears before work on place value in this book, because numbers up to 20 are in common everyday use and in the authors' opinion children can be shown how they are written down, before they gain an understanding of why they are written so. The number words are important in reading their subsequent work in mathematics.

Previous knowledge required

Numerals 1 to 10, counting to ten, number words one to ten (some will help in mastering words like 'fourteen' and 'sixteen').

Resources needed for Lesson 1

Large flashcards with numerals 1 to 20 on them, Copymaster 6, bingo base boards made up from Copymaster 7, and counters or buttons (a board and 6 counters for every child), book of number rhymes including 'One two buckle my shoe', a number track (see right) big enough for all the class to see.

Resources needed for Lesson 2

Strips of squared paper with twenty squares, Copymasters 8 and 9, 20-sided dice (one for each pair of children).

20
19
18
17
16
15
14
13
12
11
10
9
8
7
6
5
4
3
2
1

Resources needed for Lesson 3

Large flashcards with the words for all the numbers from one to twenty on them, Copymaster 10, four sets of dominoes with numerals and words on them up to twenty: some are shown below.

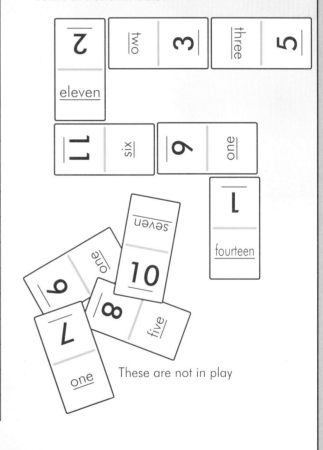

These are not in play

Teaching the lessons

Lesson 1 ①

Key questions

What does this (a numeral from 1 to 20) say?

Vocabulary

Oral response to the numerals 1 to 20.

Introduction 15min

▓ Display the number track and teach the children some number rhymes that use numbers up to 20, including 'One, two, buckle my shoe'. Once they know the rhyme, recite it again a couple of times, pointing to the numerals on the number track as the rhyme goes along.

Activities 35min

 Ask each child to complete **Copymaster 6**.

8

Give every child a bingo base board and six counters or buttons. Shuffle the large flashcards with numerals 1 to 20 on them, and then place them face down in a pile. Hold up one at a time so that the children can see it. They can call out the number and look for it on their card. If they have the number called they cover it with a counter. When some children call 'Bingo' all the children can hand their card to someone else and the game can be played again. Play the game through three or four times.

Closing the lesson
5 min

 Hold up the large numeral flashcards in turn and go around the class letting each child call out an answer.

Assessment

Child performance	Teacher action
Cannot name numerals above 10	Give more counting and matching activities
Can recognise numerals but shows hesitation	Give more practice with numeral flashcards
Knows all numerals to 20 and beyond	Move on to the next lesson

Lesson 2 ②

Key questions
Can you write the number 16?

Vocabulary
Numeral, oral number names from 1 to 20.

Introduction
5 min

Give each child a strip of paper marked in squares. Ask them to complete a number track from 1 to 20.

Activities
40 min

Give each pair of children a copy of **Copymaster 8** and a 20-sided dice. Ask the children to record what they throw each time, and see who gets closest to completing a beetle in the time allowed.

Give each child a copy of **Copymaster 9** to complete.

Give the children a numeral test. Call out numbers between one and 20 and ask them to write them down on rough paper. Take the tests in for marking.

Closing the lesson
10 min

Invite children in turn to stand at the blackboard and write up numbers between one and 20 which the class call out.

Assessment

Child performance	Teacher action
Cannot write numerals to 20	Repeat activities like those in this lesson
Writes numerals but makes errors or is uncertain	Give practice in writing numerals
Competent in writing numerals to 20	Move on to the next lesson

Lesson 3 ③

Key questions
What is the word we write for this number?

Vocabulary
Eleven, twelve, thirteen, fourteen, fifteen, sixteen, seventeen, eighteen, nineteen, twenty.

Introduction
10 min

Writing on the blackboard or a large sheet of paper, show how the words 'eleven' and 'twelve' are written. Then write the suffix '-teen' and show the children all the '-teen' number words.

Activities
40 min

Give each group a set of numeral-word dominoes and allow them to place them face down, share them out and play dominoes. Check the way the dominoes are laid.

Hold up large flashcards with the words for all the numbers from one to twenty on them in turn. Allow the class to call out the number word each time.

Ask each child to complete **Copymaster 10**.

Closing the lesson
5 min

Ask two children to stand in front of the class with the number word flashcards laid out in front of them. In quick-fire succession call out a number while the children look for the word and hold it up for the class to see.

Assessment

Child performance	Teacher action
Cannot write the number words	Continue with activities like those in Lesson 3
Not yet confident with number words	Repeat activities as in Lesson 3
Shows confidence in writing number words	Move on to another theme

Homework
Ask the children to draw 24-hour digital clocks with these times on them: five-fifteen, nine-seventeen, nineteen-eleven, thirteen-ten, six-eighteen, twelve-twelve, twenty-fourteen, fourteen-sixteen, twenty-ten. They should write the time in words beneath each picture, as shown below.

nine - seventeen

THEME 4 All about ordinal number

Learning targets

On completion of this theme the children should be able to:

1 ➤➤ put small numbers in order
2 ➤➤ name positions like first, second, third
3 ➤➤ read and write abbreviations (for example, 1st) and words for positions (for example, first)

Before you start

Subject knowledge

The children may well have met both of the main ideas in ordinal number before. They need to know what comes before five or what comes after 11, for example, and that is the order numbers come in. They should also learn position words – 'first', 'second' and so on, and how we write them in abbreviated form.

Number names have two main purposes. Used in a cardinal way a number name describes the total members in a set. For example, in 'three toy cars' the 'three' is being used as a cardinal number. In counting the cars, we may though, have counted along, 'one, two, three.' In putting number names in an order we are using the numbers as ordinal. Cardinal number is very useful when the children start doing addition and subtraction of real objects. An understanding of ordinal number is essential when using the number line, where we might add three to five by jumping three steps, in order, along the line. Certainly when the children eventually get to negative numbers they will need a concept of ordinal number as this allows us to 'jump' below zero.

Previous knowledge required

Counting and numerals from one to 20.

Resources needed for Lesson 1

Strips of card on which each child can make a game track, dice and two counters for each pair

of children, Copymaster 11, 2·5cm (1in) squared paper.

Resources needed for Lesson 2

Home corner toys, video footage of athletics including the finish of running races, 'feelie' bags and coloured beads for each work group, Copymaster 12.

Resources needed for Lesson 3

Cut out large card dogs to match those on Copymaster 13, and also ten large rosettes with position and position abbreviations and words up to 'tenth' on them as shown below. Copymaster 14, painting materials and overalls.

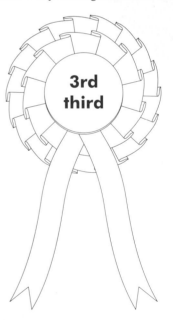

Teaching the lessons

Lesson 1   ①

Key questions

What comes before...?

What comes next?

What comes after...?

Vocabulary

Words for numbers to 20, before, after, follow, next, sequence, in order, order.

Introduction   10 min

▒ Say to the children that they should name the number that comes after the one you are going to call out. Call out a number and choose someone to answer. Do this several times, as quickly as possible.

Then repeat the procedure, asking for the number before the one called.

Activities `40min`

👤 Give each child a strip of card or a sheeet of paper on which they can draw and colour a game track from 1 to 20. They should mark up the track in one of the following ways, so that the numerals 'sit up'.

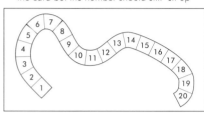

If the card is wide enough the track can trail across the card but the number should still 'sit up'

👥 In pairs the children use dice and counters and take turns to throw the dice and move first along one track, then the other.

👤 Give the children **Copymaster 11** to complete.

👥 Invite the children to make some number trails to 20 (such as the one shown below). These can be photocopied and swopped around so that other children can try them out.

Mark the start

1	2	5	8	10	14
14	3	6	13	11	6
7	4	1	6	3	2
9	5	6	7	8	3
8	20	1	10	9	19
19	18	5	11	7	4
1	6	3	12	13	14
7	9	20	2	20	15
2	11	19	18	17	16

Closing the lesson `5min`

🏁 Play 'think of a number' with the children. Choose a number under ten (for example, three). Do not tell the children what it is, but invite three children to ask a question each, to which you can answer 'yes' or 'no'. This is how it may go.

'Is it more than five?' 'No.'

'Is it after two?' 'Yes.'

'Does four come next?' 'Yes.'

Children put up their hands to offer the correct answer.

Assessment

Child performance	Teacher action
Cannot put numbers in a sequence	Give plenty of practical activity and matching and sequencing play
Can sequence numbers	Move on to the next lesson
Does the sequencing with ease and explores other patterns	Move on to the next lesson

Lesson 2 ②

Key questions

What position is this?

Which prize comes after the ... prize?

Vocabulary

First, second, third, fourth, fifth and so on up to tenth.

Introduction `10min`

🏁 Draw a short race track with a finishing line on a piece of card. Place this on a table where all the children can see it. Now place three toy cars of different colours near the finishing line. Ask the children: 'Who is the winner?' 'Which car comes next?' 'Which is last?' Then ask: 'If they each get a prize, which prize will the winner get?' The children should say 'First' and this can be the start of a discussion about first, second and third. Change the positions of the cars and ask who takes first, second and third prizes now.

Activities `45min`

🏁 Show the children some video footage of athletics including the finish of running races. Talk about who is first, second and third.

🎲 Give each group a small bag with a number of beads in it. There can be up to ten beads, including at least three colours. Allow each child a chance to pull out three beads in turn. The group should use the words first, second, and third in their discussion. They can record the work on **Copymaster 12**.

🏁 Erect a toy bus stop and place some home corner toys like teddies and dolls in a queue for the bus. Ask the children 'Who is first?' 'Which position is the doll in?' and so on up to tenth. Then ask a child to rearrange the queue. Call out instructions, for example: 'Put the rabbit first and the clown doll second', while the rest of the class look on. Try this activity with several children in turn.

Closing the lesson `10min`

🏁 Use stage blocks to make an 'Olympic podium'. Ask three children to stand on it and discuss who is first, second and third. Alter the positions of the children and discuss these. Then allow some more children the chance to go on the podium.

Assessment

Child performance	Teacher action
Child cannot use position words appropriately	Give practical activities in positioning objects with accompanying discussion
Child can use position words but not sure of some to tenth	Give more practical activities in using positions to tenth
Confident in using position words	Move on to the next lesson

Lesson 3 ③

Key questions

What does this word say?

Can you write first (or 1st)?

Vocabulary

First, second, third etc., and abbreviations 1st, 2nd, 3rd etc.

Introduction ⌗ 10 min

⊞ Place the card dogs where all the children can see them. Ask the children to pretend the dogs are in a show. Use Blu-Tack® to give them rosettes with '1st' and 'first', '2nd' and 'second' and so on, written on them as shown below.

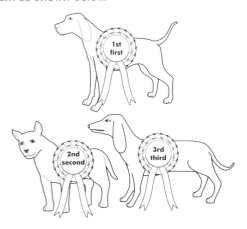

Ask the class to call out in unison the positions of the dogs in the show, as you point to them. Leave these on display for the children to use for the next activity.

Activities 40 min

👤 Ask the children to complete **Copymaster 13** using the display of dogs.

👥 Each workgroup could do the following activity in turn while the other children complete the Copymasters. Ask the children to paint a group picture showing 'first, second and third'. These could be, for example, ponies at a gymkhana, cars in a race, flowers in a flower show. The words 'first, second and third' should appear in the picture.

👤 Ask the children to complete the number story on **Copymaster 14**.

Closing the lesson 5 min

⊞ Allow the children to look at the completed paintings and talk about their depiction of the positions first, second and third.

Assessment

Child performance	Teacher action
Cannot read and write position words and abbreviations	Give practical activities, matching words and abbreviations to actual objects, and toys in the classroom.
Reads and writes position words and abbreviations	Move on to another theme but continue incidental practice
Reads and writes position words and abbreviations with ease	Move on to another theme

Homework

Draw a queue for a playground or fairground ride and write underneath each person their position in the queue.

THEME 5 Introducing place value

Learning targets

On completion of this theme the children should be able to:

1 ➡➡ count in tens and say how many tens there are in numbers up to 100

2 ➡➡ write numerals correctly for numbers up to 100

3 ➡➡ indicate how many tens and how many units there are in a number

---

Before you start

Subject knowledge

The adoption of a place value system with the use of zero for 'holding a place' was crucial in the development of modern society. Systems such as those employed by the Romans and ancient Egyptians were always limited and limiting. Thanks to mathematicians in the East and Middle East we now have the system of ten symbols that allows us all to represent any number we wish. However, as indicated in the previous theme, young children will have encountered and know numbers greater than ten. But it is likely that they will see them as separate symbols. For example '18' will not be understood at first as 1 ten and 8 units but will be seen as a whole symbol for a named number. We need, therefore to give lots of practice and opportunities for 'cracking the numbers open' in order to see the individual symbols and what they represent due to 'place'. The key idea to convey, therefore, is that where a numeral is written in relation to other numerals (its place) tells us whether it is indicating a number of 'tens' or a number of 'units or odd ones'.

Previous knowledge required

Numerals to 20, counts.

Resources needed for Lesson 1

A blank 100 square (see right); counting apparatus, for example Unifix®, Centicubes®, Multilink®, the units from Dienes® and Cuisenaire®; flashcards with the number words for thirty, forty, fifty, sixty, seventy, eighty, ninety on them; Copymaster 15.

Resources needed for Lesson 2

A blank 100 square (see below); sets of cards (enough for a set for each work group) made up from Copymaster 87 (the numerals should be stuck onto card and cut out); Copymaster 16.

On a board, flipchart or worksheet write some 'missing number' sequences for the children to complete. Here are some suggestions.

0	1	2	☐	☐	5	6	☐☐☐
20	19	☐	☐	☐	☐	13	12
26	27	☐	☐	☐	32		
35	☐	☐	38	☐	☐	☐	
99	☐	☐	☐	☐	☐	92	
47	☐	49	☐	☐	☐	54	
59	☐	☐	☐	☐	☐	52	
72	☐	74	☐	76	☐	78	

Resources needed for Lesson 3

Counting apparatus, Copymaster 17. Replies to a 'family numbers' information sheet compiled by the teacher or children and completed at home by each child. It could include questions such as: What is the date of your birthday? How many days in February? What is your lucky number? How old is the oldest person in your family?

Teaching the lessons

Vocabulary

Tens, count, continue, pattern, sequence.

Introduction
[10 min]

▓ Lead the class in counting from zero to 100 in tens and back from 100 to zero. Do this several times.

Lesson 1 ①

Key questions

Can you count in tens?

Ten, twenty … continue the pattern.

Forty is how many tens?

Activities
[40 min]

⚫⚫ Ask each group to assemble 'ten tens' using counting apparatus. Visit each group and ask them to put together, for example, sixty, thirty, ninety. Watch while they amass the tens.

👤 Give each child a blank 100 square. Ask them to count in tens along the rows and colour each 'ten' a different colour. This gives a spatial configuration to tens and one hundred to the children.

▦ Show the children flashcards with the number words 'thirty', 'forty', 'fifty', 'sixty', 'seventy', 'eighty', 'ninety' on them in turn. The spelling of 'thirty', 'forty' and 'fifty' need pointing out but thereafter the children should find the spelling easy to determine.

👤 Give the children **Copymaster 15** to complete.

Closing the lesson   5 min

▦ Call out 'two tens', 'seven tens' and so on to which the children should reply 'twenty', 'seventy' …

Assessment

Child performance	Teacher action
Cannot count in tens or say how many tens in a number	Allow plenty of practical experience with counting apparatus and an abacus and a calculator. Also do daily counting games using ten fingers.
Counts in tens but unsure when determining tens in a number	Give more practice in counting from zero to 100, saying how many tens in each number
Can count in tens and say how many tens in a number	Move on to the next lesson

Lesson 2   2

Key questions

How do we write 34?

Vocabulary

Numerals.

Introduction   10 min

▦ Write up some numbers on the blackboard, for example 25, 87, 53, 62. Invite a child to come and point out which is fifty-three, sixty-two and so on. Try this several times with different children. Then allow a child to set the challenge by writing up some numbers.

Activities   35 min

👤 Invite each child to complete the missing number sequences on the board or prepared worksheet (see 'Resources'). This can be set before the children have the full array of numbers because there are many clues to determining what is missing.

👥 Give each group a set of the cards made up from **Copymaster 87**. Then using **Copymaster 16** they can play a game of matching the words and numerals. The children should lay out all the cards face up, but mixed up. In their groups they can take turns at putting together and showing a numeral–word pair of cards.

👤 Ask each child to fill in all the numerals from 1 to 100 on a blank 100 square.

Closing the lesson   10 min

▦ Give the children a 'lightning test' by holding up some large versions of the word cards they used in the group game in the lesson and asking them to write down the numerals.

Assessment

Child performance	Teacher action
Cannot write numerals for numbers to 100	Devote two or three minutes a day to the writing of numerals for numbers until the children gain confidence
Writes numerals but makes errors	Inspect the children's errors. It may be that the child can move on to the next lesson (if the numerals are placed in the wrong order). If the wrong numerals are used or they are written wrongly the child needs more practice as above
Writes numerals accurately	Move on to the next lesson

Lesson 3   3

Key questions

How many tens are here?

Where shall I put these units?

Vocabulary

Tens, units.

Introduction   10 min

▦ Write the numerals 0 to 9 on the board. Point out to the children that when we write these we only make one mark on the page. Then write 10, 11, 12 underneath each other with the digits lined up. Draw tallies alongside these so that the children can see there is 1 ten in each number. Point out the 'odd ones' or units left. Show how these are shown by the place we put the numerals. This is how the board should look:

```
 0
 1    I
 2    I I
 3    I I I
 4    I I I I
 5    I I I I I
 6    I I I I I I
 7    I I I I I I I
 8    I I I I I I I I
 9    I I I I I I I I I
10   [I I I I I I I I I I]
11   [I I I I I I I I I I] I
12   [I I I I I I I I I I] I I
```

Activities
`35min`

❖ Invite the children to use counting apparatus to lay out the numbers that appear on **Copymaster 17**. Check what they are doing.

👤 When all the numbers have been displayed by the group ask the children to make a record of what they have done on Copymaster 17. They can then re-use the apparatus if required to construct answers to numbers they choose.

👤 Using the replies to their own 'family numbers' information sheet the children should enter up the numbers as tens and units in their workbook or on the reply sheet itself. Avoid numbers of 100 or more.

Closing the lesson
`10min`

▦ Ask the children to name the number that you say, for example if you say 'nine tens and eight units', they should say 'ninety-eight'. In quick-fire fashion do this with a range of numbers from 1 to 99.

Assessment

Child performance	Teacher action
Cannot say how many tens and units in a number	With practical apparatus show the children how to create and break up numbers showing how many tens and how many units; then repeat Lessons 2 and 3
Not confident in determining or recording tens and units	Repeat Lesson 3
Confident with the concept of tens and units	The learning targets for this theme have been met

Homework

Invite the children to take home and make up their own set of word and numeral cards based on Copymaster 87 and Copymaster 16. Set them a challenge list to complete with puzzles such as the following.

- What is the biggest number that has tens and units?
- What number has two tens and four units?
- What number is next after 45?
- 11 has the same number of tens as units. Write down all the other numbers that have the same number of tens as units.

The children can record answers to the puzzles using both numerals and number words.

Working with numbers beyond 99

Learning targets

On completion of this theme the children should be able to:

1 ➤➤ explain place value in large numbers

2 ➤➤ read numbers up to 1 million

3 ➤➤ seek out and describe large numbers in use in everyday life

Before you start

Subject knowledge

The children should be taught that place value applies, no matter how many digits there are in a number. If they have worked on Lesson 1 in Theme 5, they will understand the concept of a ten and a unit. Now it is important to extend that understanding to where digits denote hundreds and thousands. Many children find big numbers fascinating, and will take delight in being able to read them aloud. Some big numbers have special names: a hundred, thousand and million for example, and a googol – this is denoted by '1' followed by a hundred zeros!

Previous knowledge required

Tens and units.

Resources needed for Lesson 1

Counting apparatus including tens and ones (for example, Colour Factor® or Cuisenaire®); number cards made up from Copymaster 18 (a complete set for each pair of children); Copymaster 19.

Resources needed for Lesson 2

Large flashcards with the words 'hundred', 'thousand' and 'million' on them; blank 100 square; four dice or spinners with dots instead of numbers for each workgroup; rough paper.

Resources needed for Lesson 3

Workshop equipment: balances, digital clock, tape measure, calendar; *The Guinness Book of Records*; rough paper, poster paper and felt-tipped pens.

Teaching the lessons

Lesson 1   ①

Key questions

How many hundreds are there in this number?

Point to the numeral that shows thousands.

Vocabulary

Hundreds, thousands, numerals 0 to 9 (orally only).

Introduction |10min|

▓ Write up the numerals for 10 on the board. Check that the children know that there is one ten here. Write up 100 and 1000 and talk about the names we give these numbers and what each digit means.

Activities |35min|

⁘ Giving the number names orally invite the children to make up 10, 100 and 1000 using the counting apparatus. If they do this with ease tell them some other numbers to try in the range 101 to 9999.

👥 Give the children a set of number cards made up from **Copymaster 18**. Ask them to find the highest number, the lowest number, rank the numbers, group together all numbers with two tens and so on.

👤 Ask each child to complete **Copymaster 19**.

Closing the lesson |10min|

▦ Give the children four digits and ask them how many numbers they can make using all four digits, what is the largest of these, and the smallest?

Assessment

Child performance	Teacher action
Shows little under-standing of place value	Go back to Theme 5 and give the children practical activity with teacher help
Understands place value but diffident in answering	Do more work in breaking down and creating large numbers and more practice like that on Copymaster 19
Confident about place value in large numbers	Move on to the next lesson

Lesson 2

Key questions

Read out this number to me.

How do we say this number?

Vocabulary

Number words including hundred, thousand, million.

Introduction `10 min`

 Write a large number on the board, for example 120,386. Talk to the children about how many hundreds, tens and units there are in the number. Then write the number in words, thus: one hundred and twenty thousand, three hundred and eighty-six. Point out the words 'thousand' and 'hundred', which the children may not have seen before.

Place large flashcards where these can be seen by all the children. Now write up one million as 1,000,000 and the words 'one million'. Add a flashcard with 'million' on it to the others on show.

Activities `40 min`

To give the children a feel for these enormous numbers give each child a blank 100 square to fill in. When they are all laid out the number of cells will show 100 for every child in the class. The children will know that ten 100s are one thousand, so they can see how many thousands there are.

Allow the group to throw their dice and using the numbers that come up they should individually work out (without recording) the smallest number they can make and the largest they can make.

Thus if the dice read as shown below, the children should say that one thousand, two hundred and sixty-six is the smallest and six thousand, six hundred and twenty-one is the largest.

They can compare their answers and then throw again. When they can do this easily and all agree on the outcomes ask them to determine the next-to-smallest number and then the next-to-biggest number each time.

Write some numbers in words on the board for the children to copy and 'translate' into numerals.

Closing the lesson `5 min`

 Give out number cards with the numerals 1 to 7 on them to seven children. Ask any four of them to come out to the front of the class. They should stand in a row in any order showing their numeral card and the children should call out the number shown.

Ask another child with a number card to join them and allow them all to change places. The children

should call out the number again. Ask another child out and change again. Ask the final child to join them.

Swop the children's places several times allowing the children to call out the number each time. Thus this array: 5 326 should be read as five thousand, three hundred and twenty-six.

Assessment

Child performance	Teacher action
Cannot read large numbers	Do more work of the kind found in Lesson 1 in this theme
Can read numbers in hundreds but gets stuck with larger numbers	Repeat the activities tried in Lesson 2
Can read large numbers	Move on to the next lesson

Lesson 3

Key questions

Where do we find numbers like this?

How do we say this number?

Vocabulary

Names for appliances and locations where the children find large numbers in use.

Introduction `10 min`

 For fun, write up this chart and point out how many digits there are in these numbers:

ten	**10**
hundred	**100**
thousand	**1000**
ten thousand	**10 000**
hundred thousand	**100 000**
million	**1 000 000**
billion	**1 000 000 000 000**
trillion	**1 000 000 000 000 000 000**

Activities `35 min`

Allow the children to copy the chart above. They can take it home to pin on their wall.

Set up a workshop showing all the school equipment available that has numbers on it, especially including items where large numbers are in use (for example a clinical thermometer, tape measures). Ask each group to compile a booklet or poster showing our use of numbers in everyday life. The local newspaper and books like *The Guinness Book of Records* can also yield numbers for the children.

Closing the lesson `10 min`

 Ask the children to predict the biggest number that can be entered on their calculators. Let them try it out (they should fill the display with nines).

Assessment

Child performance	Teacher action
Cannot look for, find numbers or say how they are used	Allow the children to have several search sessions, looking for numbers, while continuing to work on place value and number names
Finds everyday numbers	Move on to another theme, while continuing to expose the children to experience of everyday number, including large numbers
Finds and comments on everyday numbers	Move on to another theme

Homework

Make a personal number trail using numbers in order on a long strip of paper. For example the ages of family members and pets can be entered, along with the year we are in, the number of the house, phone numbers and lucky numbers.

Investigations

- Scatter a small handful of counters or cubes and ask the children to count them. Ask them how they do this. Try this strategy for larger quantities.
- Ask how many window panes/doors/floor tiles there are in the room. Ask how we can keep a chart of our counting.
- Make bead necklaces of different numbers of beads.
- Make a collection of number rhymes, songs and stories. Have a class book of these and use them, with an appropriate display, for stimulus, discussion and practice.
- Make patterns of given numbers of pegs, beads or marbles using peg boards.
- Make a collection of simple dice board games like Snakes and Ladders and let the children play these and talk about counting on.
- Ask the children to collect pictures from magazines or comics where they have found some interesting things to count.
- Ask for the story of a counting number. For example, what can the children tell you about 'three'?

Examples might include the following: 3 comes before 4 and after 2; there are 3 bears and 3 little pigs; mummy, daddy and baby make 3; a hop, skip and jump is 3 actions; we talk about 3-course meals; there are three-wheelers; dinosaur triceratops had 3 horns; 3 is the age of a little brother or sister.

- Arrange a number hunt, where cards, some with numerals on them and some number words between, say, five and fifty or five and five hundred are placed around the hall or the corridor. The children should find the numbers and write them in order in a list. They can then check this against a master list in the classroom.
- Give the children some school facts and figures so that they can meet some number challenges. This data could include, for example, class sizes, the numbers on the registration plates of teachers' cars, and the number of hours worked each day by the school cook, the caretaker and the secretary. They can then say which class is biggest, who has the smallest number on their car, who works the longest hours, and do more finding out for themselves.

Assessment

- Using cards with single digit numbers on them, shuffle them and ask the children to say what the number is each time.
- Say a number and ask what the number is before and after it, or use a number line to show the number.
- Say two numbers and ask which is greater or lesser, or point to two numbers on a number line and ask which is the greater.

- Use rubber stamps showing, for example, birds and trees and ask the children to match one-to-one, or create matching sets of these.
- Ask the children to draw, for example, two faces, five houses and three garden gates.
- Give a child a set of small toys and ask them to make a set with the same number, one more or one fewer in it.

ADDITION AND SUBTRACTION

Understanding of cardinal number is a pre-requisite for the addition and subtraction of numbers that do not involve a solution less than zero. To be able to take, for example, a set of three objects and a set of four objects and combine them to make a set of seven uses cardinality. When we say that the difference between these two sets is one, we are also using cardinality. Such addition and subtraction problems can also be tackled using a number line, in which case an understanding of ordinality is also important.

For centuries there have been aids to computation and the abacus can be seen as a very ancient instrument to support addition and subtraction. In practical terms it is possible to discern a common sequence of responses when children start working with addition. It is common for children to count out a set, and then a second set. These are then combined to give a solution. At first the child will commonly count out the combination starting from one. Later, when the child is more experienced, the combination will be done by counting on from the last number in the first set. These are useful sorts of observation for they can often give the teacher a clue as to any misunderstandings.

It is important that children see, from the start, that the order in which sets are combined does not matter; that is, they need to see that addition is commutative. An important corollary of this is that they come to see, early on, that it does matter about the order when it comes to subtraction – subtraction is not commutative. There are a number of important aspects to look for in subtraction. These are comparing, take-away and complementary addition. When comparing, children are expected to be using the ideas of more and less than. In taking away, we are looking for the number left over – a common experience of children is having a pack of sweets and eating some of them. By complementary addition is meant the approach commonly taken in shops where the 'difference' between money proferred and the cost of the article, as represented by one's change, and is calculated by adding. So, for example, the difference between seven pencils and three pencils can be obtained by adding on from three – 'four, five, six, seven' – giving four steps as the difference.

Introducing addition

Learning targets

On completion of this theme the children should be able to:

1 ➤➤ add more to a group of objects

2 ➤➤ put sets or groups of objects together to make a total and match this to a numeral

3 ➤➤ use addition vocabulary and make their own record of additions

Before you start

Subject knowledge

This is the first step that children take, that they themselves will later associate with the work of manipulating numbers. It is therefore vital that this learning is achieved successfully. The children need to know that when we place more in a set or put sets together we are doing what is called addition. These are 'sums' (no other kind of operation is strictly a 'sum') and the total here is known as 'the sum'. Note that the idea of zero as 'an empty set' can be introduced in Lesson 2.

Previous knowledge required

Counting to 10, vocabulary like 'more', numbers (both words and numerals) from one to ten.

Resources needed for Lesson 1

Small objects and toys for counting and addition, Copymasters 20 and 21.

Resources needed for Lesson 2

Small objects and toys for counting and addition, cards with numerals 1 to 9 on them; dice with faces marked one dot to five dots with the remaining side blank (a pair of dice to each pair of children); board games (one for each pair of children) which could be bought-in games like Snakes and Ladders or games made up from Copymaster 88 or 89; Copymaster 22.

Resources needed for Lesson 3

Small objects and toys for counting and addition, rough paper on which to make a record of this work.

On a board, flipchart or worksheet write some picture 'sums' for the children to copy and complete. Here are examples.

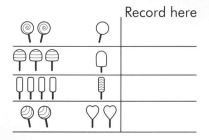

Teaching the lessons

Lesson 1   ❶

Key questions

What is one more?

… and two more make …?

Vocabulary

Words for numbers to ten, more.

Introduction   5 min

▓ Ask a child to stand at the front of the class. Give the child a book. Now give the child another book and say 'and one more makes?' Do this again and again until ten is reached.

Activities   35 min

👤 Ask everyone to make a strip showing birds on the wall using **Copymaster 20**. (These can be made up for the children to save lesson time.) They should fold all but one of the birds back and then fold each up in turn saying '… and one more makes …' each time.

▓ Ask everyone to hold their strip of birds sitting on the wall and fold all the birds back. Now they should fold up one bird and then two more saying, 'and two more makes' until nine is reached. Now try the same exercise with the children pushing up three birds this time, starting with only one bird on the wall.

👤 Ask the children to complete **Copymaster 21**.

Closing the lesson   10 min

▓ Hand around ten toys to different children. Allow them to bring them to the front and display them in turn, saying '… and one more makes …' until all ten are on display.

20

Assessment

Child performance	Teacher action
Cannot add more to a group of things	Allow children practice in making sets that they count. Drop one more into a set and ask how many now? This should continue in short sessions until the children anticipate the number outcome
Adds one more successfully, thereafter less confident	Move on to next lesson but continue to practice '… and X more makes …?'
Adds more to a group of things	Move on to the next lesson

Lesson 2 ②

Key questions

If we put this set with that set how many altogether?

Vocabulary

Total, sum, numeral.

Introduction 10 min

Using small toys ask two children to take a small number each. Allow them to hold them up to show the class. The toys should then be physically placed together. Ask the children what the total is. Try this again and again with different children and different numbers of toys.

Activities 30 min

Ask the children to set out counters or small bricks to show the sets depicted on **Copymaster 22**. They can then attach a numeral card to the total. They can show you the groups set out and their numeral card answers.

Ask the children to play a track game such as **Copymaster 88** or **89**, throwing both dice and adding the scores before making a move. Point out that the blank side of the dice means no dots, nought or zero dots.

Closing the lesson 10 min

Ask the children to add two small numbers in their heads. Present some addition vocabulary while giving them challenges. For example, say: 'Sum the following'; 'What is the total'; 'Try this addition'.

Assessment

Child performance	Teacher action
Cannot find the sum of two sets of objects	Give more practical experience of placing two or more sets of objects together and finding the total
Finds the sum but has to count through from one and sometimes repeat counts	Work at combining sets and finding totals until more confident
Finds the sum, can conserve small numbers and count on.	Move on to the next lesson

Lesson 3 ③

Key questions

What is the sum of … and … ?
Do this addition, what is the total?

Vocabulary

Total, sum, add, addition, plus.

Introduction 10 min

Hold up two numeral flashcards between 0 and 5 and ask the children to call out the total. Allow them to use fingers for the counting if they wish. Do this for several pairs of numbers, and then three numbers, with totals not exceeding 10.

Activities 30 min

Allow children access to small toys, counters, bricks and other things to group for additions. Ask them to make up their own additions and make a full record of them on the rough paper. Their records may look something like this:

   I I I   I I   I I I I I

Ask each child to draw or colour and complete the picture additions on the board or prepared worksheet.

Closing the lesson 10 min

Ask the children to think of all the ways they can to make three. It could be one and one and one, or one and two, or three and zero. Now choose another number and ask for ways to make it.

Assessment

Child performance	Teacher action
Does not use addition vocabulary and has problems in recording addition.	Repeat the kinds of activities done in Lessons 1 and 2
Not confident in doing or recording addition	Do some more work like that in Lesson 2 and then work again on Lesson 3
Does and records addition with confidence	Move on to another theme

Homework

Allow children to take home a game board such as Copymaster 88 or 89, and spinners (Copymaster 90), to play at home.

Adding to 10

Learning targets

On completion of this theme the children should be able to:

1 ➤➤ set out additions using words and numbers

2 ➤➤ set out additions using the equals sign and the addition symbol

3 ➤➤ do additions to ten including 'missing numbers'

Before you start

Subject knowledge

Following work on putting sets of objects together and the use of numerals in addition, this theme is concerned with enabling children to write additions using mathematical conventions and using the vocabulary of mathematics (for example, plus, equals, sum). They should be able to use the equals sign and the sign for addition. Note that the important point about 'equals' is that the items on one side of the 'equals' sign should 'match' (that is give the same total) as those on the other side of the 'equals' sign. The children should also be able to set down additions across or down the page. However, in doing horizontal and then vertical presentations we need to be aware of a number of possibly confusing issues. In, for example, portraying the addition of seven and three horizontally, we are capitalising on the left to right reading experience. However, in moving to vertical presentation we are asking for a different reading orientation and, when we get to numbers greater than nine an appreciation of place value. Conventionally, horizontal presentation is employed for those number bonds we will come to know by heart and vertical presentation for those that we will have to compute.

Previous knowledge required

Numerals, the operation of addition, some addition vocabulary.

Resources needed for Lesson 1

Flashcards for each group with the words 'and', 'makes' and 'altogether' on them, Copymaster 23.

Resources needed for Lesson 2

Dice with numerals on them as shown below.

Copymaster 24 (two copies for each child), card strips as shown below (two for each child).

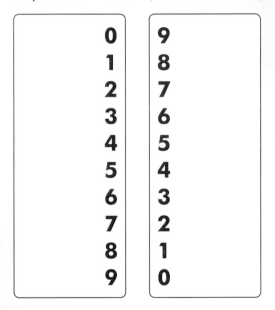

Resources needed for Lesson 3

Calculators, number trails, Copymaster 25.

Teaching the lessons

Lesson 1 ①

Key questions

How many altogether?

Vocabulary

Numerals to 10, and, makes, altogether.

Introduction [10 min]

▓ Using large flashcards with the words 'and' 'makes' and 'altogether' on them and some objects that can be set out for counting. place a small group on a table where all the children can see it. Place the 'and' card next to the group and then put down another group of objects. Now place the 'makes' card down. Then pick up the two groups and physically put them together after the 'makes' card. Put the 'altogether' card at the end. Allow all the children to read aloud the numbers of objects and the words several times. Do the same exercise with several more groups of objects where the total will not exceed ten. This is how a sample calculation should look.

Activities
[35 min]

🔵 Invite each group to allow every child to have a go at doing calculations as the teacher did in the introduction. They need to have a set of 'and', 'makes' and 'altogether' flashcards and some objects to count.

👤 Ask the children to complete **Copymaster 23**.

▦ In front of the whole class hold up a small number of objects in one hand, so that the children can see them. Do the same in the other hand, and then ask 'how many altogether?' The children should call out the answer. Use the same groups of objects, but swop hands and ask the same question. Now do the same challenge with different groups of objects, up to a total of ten. Swop hands each time so that the children come to understand that the order of the groups does not affect the total.

Closing the lesson
[10 min]

▦ To give the children the opportunity to try addition in the abstract, give them a mental test. Place one object on the desk. Call out: 'And one more makes?; And four more make?' Ask the children to write down the answers. Try some more challenges with two or three objects on the desk.

Assessment

Child performance	Teacher action
Cannot do additions using words and numbers	Give the children plenty of practical experience of counting, placing groups of objects together and counting totals. Then repeat the activities tackled in this lesson
Can do additions but lacks confidence	Give more practice at activities like those in this lesson
Uses counting on to do additions and beginning to do addition mentally	Move on to the next lesson

Lesson 2 ②

Key questions

What is the sum of … and …?

What is the total?

If we add … and … what is the answer?

Vocabulary

Plus, add, equals, total, sum, words for numbers.

Introduction
[10 min]

▦ Write up on the board the following:

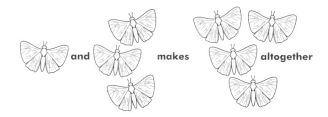

Explain that in mathematics, we use special signs and symbols in calculations. Write the numeral '2' and say that this is the symbol used for two. Write up an addition sign and tell the children that this means 'add' or 'plus' and it is used when two sets are put together. (This notation is also used when we 'step' along a number line). Then write an 'equals' sign and explain where this goes in the calculation. Put in the signs in the calculation set out on the board, as shown below.

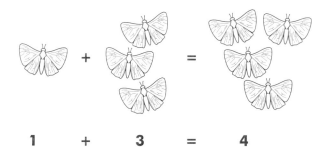

$$1 \quad + \quad 3 \quad = \quad 4$$

If there is time, write more additions, inviting individual children to come and put in the signs. Leave the examples on the board.

Activities
[30 min]

👥 Using two dice with numerals on them the children, in pairs, should take turns to throw them and then write out an addition on a large sheet of paper placed between them. The sums can be made using the numbers that have come up on the dice and the addition and equals signs. Check the work the children are doing.

👤 Ask each child to complete two copies of **Copymaster 24**. Each child will need two card strips made up as in 'Resources'.

23

They should place the strips alongside one another as shown below:

They then record $0 + 0 = 0$, and move the right hand strip down so that the next numerals are lined up. This should give them $0 + 1 = 1$ and $1 + 0 = 1$. They then move the right hand strip down again, completing additions using all the pairs of numerals showing, and so on until the cards lie exactly alongside one another for their whole length. On the Copymasters, the children should have recorded a range of examples of number bonds to nine.

Closing the lesson ⬛ 5 min
▦ Review with the children the work they have done using the card strips. Point out the patterns in the numbers.

Assessment

Child performance	Teacher action
Cannot set out additions using the equals sign and the addition symbol	Give more practice using activities like those in this lesson.
Uses symbols but not with confidence	Give more practice using activities like those in this lesson
Confident in the use of symbols	Move on to the next lesson

Lesson 3 ③

Key questions
What is this missing number?
What is the sum of … and …?

Vocabulary
Addition, add, sum, total.

Introduction ⬛ 10 min
▦ Write up these examples on the board to show children what we mean by 'missing numbers'.

$$3 + \boxed{} = 5$$

$$\boxed{} + 2 = 4$$

$$\boxed{} + 2 + 1 = 6$$

Point out to the children that the missing number's position can be anywhere in the sum.

Activities ⬛ 35 min
▦▦ Put twenty 'missing number' additions in two columns of ten each on the board for the children to try. Ask the children to agree that one of them writes out and tries the first column one to ten, while the other does the second column. Then they can swop and try checking each other's work. At the end give them a calculator to run a final check.

▦ The children should complete the number trails on **Copymaster 25**.

Closing the lesson ⬛ 10 min
▦ Play 'What do I need to make …?' Show the children a flashcard with a number on it, say 7, and then say 'I have five, what do I need to make seven?' Try several puzzles like this.

Assessment

Child performance	Teacher action
Cannot do additions to ten including 'missing numbers'	Allow plenty of practical addition and repeat some of the activities found in Lessons 2 and 3 to give the children more practice
Can add to ten but sometimes gets stuck on missing numbers	Do more work on the idea of a missing number and 'What's missing?' puzzles
Can add to ten and find missing numbers	The learning targets for this theme have been met

Homework
Give the children more number trails like those on Copymaster 25 to try. Ask them to invent a number trail where the total is up to 10 and draw it with a black felt tip pen so that it can be photocopied. The children can bring them in to school and they can be copied for their classmates to try out.

Introducing subtraction

Learning targets

On completion of this theme the children should be able to:

1 ➡➡ take items away from a group and say what has happened
2 ➡➡ take away a number of items from a group and give an answer which they can match with a numeral
3 ➡➡ use subtraction vocabulary and make a record of subtractions

Before you start

Subject knowledge

It is likely that addition will be presented to the children before subtraction. It can be argued that young children are much more aware of the idea of 'taking away' because of their life experiences, including for example, their toys being snatched by another child. The concepts of addition and subtraction are inextricably linked, and the authors' experience indicates that most children competent in addition, master subtraction next without difficulty. The important ideas include the idea of difference. It is important to note that some people have their own methods of determining difference, including counting on. Thus, finding the difference can encompass 'more than' as well as 'less than'.

Previous knowledge required

Everyday life experience of 'taking things away'; reading and writing numbers to ten.

Resources needed for Lesson 1

Items of PE equipment, soft toys, objects for counting, strip of card cats on a wall for each child, made up from Copymaster 26, book of nursery rhymes which involve 'taking away' (for example, 'Five green speckled frogs', 'Five little ducks went swimming one day').

Resources needed for Lesson 2

Objects for counting, flashcards for each group with the words 'take away' and 'leaves' on them, numeral cards to ten.

Resources needed for Lesson 3

Objects for concrete subtractions for example, items of classroom equipment or small toys. There should be at least 10 groups of objects (each group not exceeding 10), cards each with 'subtract' and a numeral on them, Copymaster 27. Homework: Copymaster 28.

Teaching the lessons

Lesson 1　　①

Key questions

If I take away … how many are left?
… take away … leaves …?

Vocabulary

Take away, leaves.

Introduction　　15 min

▦ Ask two children to stand out in front of the others. Ask how many children are there. Move one child away and say: 'If I take away one child how many are left?' Now ask another child to join the original two, and take away one child and then another. Place the children back again and this time take away two at once. Continue with the activity up to a starting group of five children.

Do the same exercise with footballs or trainers or other items of PE equipment, taking one example at a time. Repeat the subtractions a third time with soft toys. This time ask a child to act as teacher and say, for example, 'If Melanie takes one toy away, how many are left? If necessary repeat the toy subtractions using other children as 'teachers'.

Activities　　30 min

▦▦ Allow each pair of children to have five items (all the same kind of thing) to use for counting. Ask them to take turns at being teacher and repeat what was done at the beginning of the lesson.

▦ Give each child a strip of card cats on a wall made up from **Copymaster 26**. Ask them to sit all the cats up on the wall. Invite them to fold one cat back and 'take it away.' Ask what this leaves. Give the children other challenges in subtraction setting any number of cats on the wall to start with, from one to five. When all cats are taken away there are 'none' left.

▦ Teach the children some rhymes involving 'taking away'. These can be acted out by the children.

Closing the lesson 10 min

 Ask the children to hold up five fingers, take away one and show and say how many are left. Repeat this game several times.

Assessment

Child performance	Teacher action
Cannot take things away from a group and say what has happened to the number of things in the group	Check the children's counting skills and give each child individual attention in physically removing or 'taking away' items from a group
Can take away	Give a practical session to consolidate what has been learned before moving on to the next lesson
Shows confidence, and works quickly on take away	Move on to the next lesson

Lesson 2 ②

Key questions

What number is left?

How many are taken away?

Vocabulary

Take away, leaves, left, number, numeral.

Introduction 10 min

 Do some practical take aways, using totals up to ten this time, and items of class equipment like chairs and exercise books as well as the children themselves.

Activities 35 min

 Allow each pair of children to take turns at practical take aways, using pencils, crayons or other class equipment.

 Set out a take away calculation using a number of exercise books. Place copies of the flashcards 'take away' and 'leaves' in the appropriate places as shown here:

takeaway   leaves

Read the calculation to the children. Hold up the flashcards and read them again. Show the children several more examples.

 Allow each group a copy of the two flashcards and ten items to use for calculations. Give each group a set of flashcards with the numerals 0 to 9 on them. Allow the children to each have a turn at setting out a subtraction group, from which they physically take some away, setting out a numeral answer. The other members of the group should look on while they talk it through.

Closing the lesson 10 min

 Hold up numeral flashcards and ask the children 'What is one less?' 'Two less?' 'I started with eight, I have two left, how many have I taken away?' and other similar mental challenges.

Assessment

Child performance	Teacher action
Cannot take away a number of items from a group and give an answer which they can match with a numeral	Give more practical take away experiences like those in Lesson 1 and Lesson 2
Can use a numeral answer in take aways but not yet confident	Give more practice in setting a numeral answer to take aways
Can take away with confidence and use numeral answers	Move on to the next lesson

Lesson 3 ③

Key questions

Can you write the number for how many are left?

Vocabulary

Subtract, number, numeral.

Introduction 10 min

 Draw a group of objects on the board. Underneath, write the word 'subtract' and a numeral, like this:

subtract 2   **leaves**

Ask the children for the answer. Draw the answer group of objects. Work on a couple more examples.

Activities 35 min

 Give each child a piece of paper with a fold down the middle. Ask them to draw a group of things on one side of the fold (it can be any number up to ten). A theme can be set for the pictures (for example, a wildlife park or sea-side if you wish). Underneath the picture they should write 'subtract' and then a numeral. On the other side of the fold they can draw the group of things that are left. These can be set aside until the end of the lesson.

Before the class set up at least 10 groups of objects (numbered one to 10) around the room, and by each group set a card which says 'subtract' and a numeral.

 Invite the children to go around in pairs, visiting the groups in any order, but recording their answers as a picture or a number in order on a piece of paper.

 Check the answers with the class.

 Ask each child to complete **Copymaster 27**.

Closing the lesson

▓ Fold back the 'answer half' on each of the picture subtractions the children drew at the beginning of the lesson. Hold up the subtraction pictures in turn, allowing the children to call out the answers. Fold out the 'answer half' each time to confirm the outcome. These pictures can be put on the wall in a frieze.

Assessment

Child performance	Teacher action
Cannot use subtraction vocabulary and make a record of subtractions	Give the children more practical experience of 'take away' before re-introducing the vocabulary and asking them to make a record
Uses subtraction vocabulary but lacks confidence	Give more practice of work like that done in Lesson 3
Uses vocabulary and records with confidence	The learning targets for this theme have been met

Homework

Give the children **Copymaster 28** which is a subtraction game, to try at home.

Subtracting to 10

Learning targets

On completion of this theme the children should be able to:

1 ➡➡ set out subtractions using the equals and subtraction signs
2 ➡➡ do subtractions to ten including 'missing numbers'
3 ➡➡ find the difference between two numbers that are less than ten

Before you start

Subject knowledge

In this theme the children will be learning how to set out subtraction calculations using both the 'subtraction and 'equals' signs. They will also associate 'finding the difference' between two numbers with subtraction. It cannot be over-emphasised how important vocabulary is in trying to explore computation like this. Words and phrases like 'difference', 'less', 'more' and 'take away' are all in common parlance, yet in mathematics they have particular meanings. It is important to use as many alternatives as possible in each case and take time to explore, use and define them with the help of the children.

Previous knowledge required

Practical subtraction using real objects, counting to ten.

1
2
3
4
5
6
7
8
9
10
11
12
13
14
15
16
17
18
19
20

Resources needed for Lesson 1

Large sheets of rough paper, laces or pieces of coloured wools, cards with numerals from one to ten on them and cards with subtraction and equals signs on them (enough for each group to have plenty), Copymasters 29 and 30.

Resources needed for Lesson 2

Blank 100 squares (one for each child), large number flashcards and cards with subtraction and equals signs on them, Copymaster 31.

Resources needed for Lesson 3

Floor number track as shown, Copymaster 32, dice or spinners with numbers up to ten on them (spinners can be made from the appropriate outlines on Copymaster 90).

Teaching the lessons

Lesson 1 ❶

Key questions

What does this sign tell us?

How do we write the sign for 'equals'?

Vocabulary

Subtract, subtraction, equals.

Introduction ⏱ 10 min

▦ Show the children the large flashcard with the subtraction sign on it and tell them what it is. Place the two large sheets of paper where the children can see them. (If this proves impossible do this exercise on the board). Place a numeral card on the left hand paper, and between the papers a smaller numeral card and the subtraction sign. Now join a lace to the numeral across the gap and to an answer card on the other sheet of paper. Create several examples and tell the children that this is called mapping. Here are some examples:

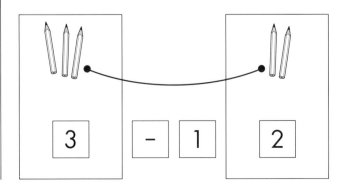

Activities `40min`

👤 Ask the children to complete **Copymaster 29** where they are asked to draw in the lines to complete some mapping. They will also be interpreting the subtraction sign.

▦ Remind the children of the 'equals' sign and show them the flashcard. Point out that the totals on each side of an equals sign must be the same. Show them again the subtraction sign on a flashcard. Write up some example subtractions on the board, putting in the subtraction and equals signs as shown below.

7	subtract	4	equals	3
7	–	4	=	3
5	–	2	=	?

⚫⚫ Give each group a pile of numeral cards and equals and subtraction cards. Invite them to make up some subtractions. All the children can then look at other groups' efforts and check them as they move around.

👤 Ask the children to complete the subtractions on **Copymaster 30**, putting in the signs and answers.

Closing the lesson `10min`

▦ Write out the calculations found on Copymaster 30 on the board, asking a different child out to complete each one. If you wish, the children, in pairs, can check one another's work.

Assessment

Child performance	Teacher action
Cannot do mapping or recognise subtraction and equals signs	Give more mapping practice and work at using the flashcards with the sign on them, while talking through the calculations and using the words subtract and equals.
Can interpret subtraction and equals signs	Give more practice in inserting the signs into calculations
Can write down and use the signs for equals and subtract.	Move on to the next lesson

Lesson 2 ②

Key questions

Subtract … from …

What is the missing number here?

Vocabulary

Subtract, subtraction.

Introduction `10min`

▦ Invite the children to count down from ten. Point out

that the outcome is the same as first taking away one, then two, then three, and so on from ten. Begin a 'mathematical story of ten (10)' thus: $10 - 1 = 9$; $10 - 2 = 8$; etc.

Activities `35min`

⚫⚫ Invite each group to write down more facts they know about ten, particularly in relation to subtraction. These can all be compared and pooled. Remind the children that they can have facts like this:

$10 - 1 - 1 - 1 - 1 - 1 - 1 - 1 - 1 - 1 - 1 = 0$

👤 Give each child a blank 100 square. They can colour in the rows or columns to represent subtractions from ten, and make a record of them as shown below.

✗	✗	✗							
				✗	✗	✗	✗	✗	

$10 - 3 = 7$
$10 - 5 = 5$

▦ Using number flashcards and a subtraction and equals sign flashcard set up a subtraction with a missing number in it as shown below, using children to hold the number cards.

Ask another child to come to the front and find the missing number card and place it in the calculation.

Do this several times, changing the position of the missing number.

👤 Ask the children to complete **Copymaster 31**, filling in the numbers that are missing.

Closing the lesson `10 min`

 Call out some subtractions with missing numbers so that the children can work out what is missing (for example, eight subtract what leaves two?).

Assessment

Child performance	Teacher action
Cannot do subtractions to ten including 'missing numbers'	Give more practice in practical subtraction. Return to Theme 9
Can do subtractions but takes time to find answers	Give more practice in activities like those in this lesson
Can quickly and confidently work with subtraction to ten	Move on to the next lesson

Lesson 3 ③

Key questions

What is the difference between … and …?

Vocabulary

Difference, lesser, greater.

Introduction `5 min`

 Explain to the children that when we are comparing two different numbers we can subtract the smaller from the larger and call this the difference between them. Write some example numbers on the blackboard.

Activities `40 min`

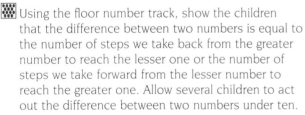 The children can take turns to throw both dice or spin both spinners and find the difference between the numbers.

Using the floor number track, show the children that the difference between two numbers is equal to the number of steps we take back from the greater number to reach the lesser one or the number of steps we take forward from the lesser number to reach the greater one. Allow several children to act out the difference between two numbers under ten.

Ask the children to complete **Copymaster 32** where they are finding the difference.

Closing the lesson `10 min`

Give individual quick-fire challenges to the children such as, 'Give me two numbers with a difference of three.'

Assessment

Child performance	Teacher action
Cannot find the difference between two numbers that are less than ten	Work on practical activities with the children until they have more confidence; then re-introduce the idea of difference
Finds the difference between two numbers	Give more practice at working at speed
finds the difference with ease and rapidity	The learning targets for this theme have been met

Homework

Invite the children to use an old cereal box to create a take-away game for young children. If the box is carefully opened out and refixed inside out it can be covered and will take paint well. Some suggested ideas for designs the children might try are shown below.

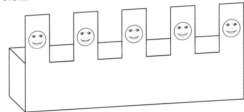

Here the smiley faces can be taken away by being folded back, or a soft ball or beanbag can be thrown at them. A 'hit' means the face is 'taken away'.

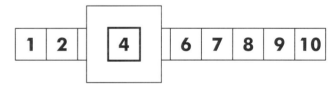

This window strip can be used to show a starting number, for example '4'. Then, if the challenge is 'subtract 2' the window is moved down the track in two jumps to arrive at the answer '2'.

Adding and subtracting to 20

Learning targets

On completion of this theme the children should be able to:

1 ➤➤ add and subtract using numbers to 20
2 ➤➤ link addition and subtraction
3 ➤➤ know common number bonds to 20

Before you start

Subject knowledge

The quick recall of all additions and subtractions up to 20 is a powerful tool to use in more complex calculations. This is the final target here, and on the way the children should continue to learn the conventions of writing additions and subtractions both horizontally and vertically. Note that this theme can be tackled before children have been introduced to place value. It is assumed, however, that the children will be able to cope with zero as denoting an empty set.

Previous knowledge required

Addition and subtraction to 10, numbers to 20.

Resources needed for Lesson 1

Floor or large size number track to 20; flashcards with additions and subtractions on them using numbers less than 20 (make one card for each workgroup and include twenty calculations on each card – cards can be made up from Copymaster 33, if you wish); counting apparatus; individual number tracks from 0 to 20; a six-sided dice for each pair of children; Copymaster 34.

Resources needed for Lesson 2

Two dice or spinners for each pair of children (spinners can be made up from Copymaster 94), Copymaster 35.

Resources needed for Lesson 3

Cards with a number from 11 to 20 on them (make up enough for each pair of children to have a card); a large collection of dice including particularly those that are twelve- and eight-sided (twenty-sided dice can be used for subtractions; Copymaster 36. Homework: Copymaster 37.

Teaching the lessons

Lesson 1 ①

Key questions

What is the sum of these numbers?

What is … subtract (or minus) …?

How can you make … using these numbers and doing addition and/or subtraction?

Vocabulary

Add, addition, calculation, subtract, minus, subtraction.

Introduction `10min`

▦ Using a large floor number track to 20 or a track that can be held up for all the children to see, use it as an aid to demonstrate addition and subtraction to 20.

Activities `40min`

� Invite each group to work out the answers to challenges on their card using a number track. Check each child makes several calculations.

👤 Using counting apparatus and individual number tracks from 0 to 20 allow the children to complete **Copymaster 34**.

👥 Each pair of children has a dice and they take turns at throwing the dice three times, summing the outcome and taking away the smallest number thrown to achieve a result. They should record this total and on the next go try to make another number between one and 18. The winner is the one who makes all numbers two to 17 first.

Closing the lesson `10min`

▦ Tell the children that you are going to call out some calculations; they should compute the answer and do some actions. For example, if the number is less than ten they should put their right hand up, more than ten their left hand. They can stand up if the answer is two less than the last answer. They can stand on one leg if the answer is in the pattern of counting in twos, and so on.

Assessment

Child performance	Teacher action
Cannot add and subtract using numbers to 20	Recap Themes 8 and 10 until the children's knowledge of addition and subtraction to ten is secure. Gradually introduce numbers 11 to 20 into calculations
Can add and subtract to 20 but requires more practice	Give practice in practical settings then move on to the next lesson
Can add and subtract to 20	Move on to the next lesson
Links addition and subtraction	Move on to the next lesson
Can 'play' with the numbers and see the links at a glance	Move on to the next lesson

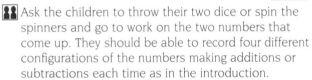

Lesson 2 ②

Key questions

Can you convert this addition to a subtraction using the same figures?

Vocabulary

Subtraction, addition.

Introduction `10min`

▓ Write 2 + 3 on the board. Point out that 3 + 2 also sums to 5. Write 5 – 2 = 3 and 5 – 3 = 2 to show the same numbers appear in these calculations, and that addition and subtraction are linked. Ask a volunteer to work out all the possible presentations of addition and subtraction using another set of numbers.

Activities `35min`

👥 Ask the children to throw their two dice or spin the spinners and go to work on the two numbers that come up. They should be able to record four different configurations of the numbers making additions or subtractions each time as in the introduction.

👤 Ask each child to complete **Copymaster 35** which links addition and subtraction.

▓ Demonstrate on the board that additions and subtractions can be written down the page. Write several examples, and allow the children to change some calculations set out horizontally and set them out vertically in their books.

Closing the lesson `10min`

▓ Write three numbers on the board and ask individual children to create and call out a calculation, while the others listen. Thus 8, 5, 3, would become eight equals five plus three; 12, 7, 5, could be '12 minus seven equals five'.

Assessment

Child performance	Teacher action
Cannot link addition and subtraction	Give more practice including a page of additions, then a page of subtractions which use the same digits. Discuss these with the children

Lesson 3 ③

Key questions

What is the sum of … and …?
Give me six ways of making six, sixteen … etc.

Vocabulary

Number bond, pairs of numbers.

Introduction `10min`

▓ Tell the children that it is a great help in their mathematics if they can recall pairs of numbers that have a given total. Ask for pairs of numbers that make five. These are: 0 + 5, 1 + 4, 2 + 3, 3 + 2, 4 + 1, and 5 + 0. Now ask for ways of making ten.

Activities `35min`

👥 Each pair of children takes a number out of a hat and writes down the pairs of numbers that make it.

🎲 Allow the children to play with a large collection of dice including those that are eight-, twelve- and twenty-sided. They can create additions and subtractions for another group to solve using these.

👤 Ask the children to complete **Copymaster 36**.

Closing the lesson `10min`

▓ Give the children a mental test, where you give the total and one of the constituent numbers and they write down the other number, such as the number 15 can be made from 8 and ? (answer 7).

Assessment

Child performance	Teacher action
Does not know common number bonds to 20	Give more practice including dice games and work with counting apparatus, before attempting mental addition
Knows bonds to 20 but does not have fast recall	Give speed tests until the children are able to recall facts quickly
Has instant recall of number bonds to 20	The learning targets for this theme have been met

Homework

Ask the children to make a set of cards from **Copymaster 37**. They can match the number pairs and totals, playing a memory game where all cards are face down and they turn up two to match.

Adding and subtracting to 100

Learning targets

On completion of this theme the children should be able to:

1 ➡➡ do practical addition and subtraction using mathematical apparatus

2 ➡➡ work with addition and subtraction to 100

3 ➡➡ solve and create number 'stories'

Before you start

Subject knowledge

The children will already have met numbers with two digits and know that in each number the digits denote the number of tens and the number of units. Using their knowledge of how the numbers can be set out as a number of tens and a number of units they can begin adding and subtracting, exchanging ten units for a ten where appropriate. They should soon be able to do this without apparatus. This is also an opportunity to help children make approximations and anticipate what order of answer to expect.

In Lesson 1 the focus is taken to be addition to 100. The same activities can be adapted to offer children practice in subtraction to 100.

Previous knowledge required

Place value, numbers to 100, addition and subtraction to 20.

Resources needed for Lesson 1

Mathematical apparatus suitable for setting out tens and ones in tens and units, Copymaster 38.

Resources needed for Lesson 2

Mathematical apparatus suitable for setting out tens and ones in tens and units, Copymaster 39.

Resources needed for Lesson 3

Mathematical apparatus suitable for setting out tens and ones in tens and units; flashcards with street names on them; bundles of old envelopes to serve as letters and a mail 'sack' for use as described in the introduction; Copymaster 40; computation cards with additions or subtractions to 100 on them; two sets of matching answer cards for the Bingo game as described in Closing the lesson.

Teaching the lessons

Lesson 1 ①

Key questions

Which should we add (or subtract) first?

Set out the numbers showing tens and units.

How many tens in your answer?

Vocabulary

Tens, units, add, subtract.

Introduction 10min

▦ Show the children by drawing on the board, or using mathematical apparatus if they can all see it, how to set out a number up to ten, and then some numbers exceeding ten. Set challenges for individual children to do while the others look on. For example, 'Can you set out the number sixty?' 'Lay out the tens and units in 35.' 'Can you say what number I have set out here?' Then set out two numbers having tens and units, where the units can be added together to create a number less than ten. Thus 21 + 14 can be set out as shown below and the answer can be computed. Try out several examples.

Activities 40min

⚄ Write up ten additions involving numbers up to 99 where the units added will not exceed a total of nine and where the tens also will not exceed nine in total. Ask each group to use the mathematical apparatus to set out the calculation and then arrange the answer. Each child should have at least one go at doing this while the others look on.

👤 Ask the children to complete **Copymaster 38**, where they can draw in the apparatus they have used.

33

Closing the lesson $\boxed{5\text{min}}$

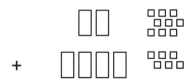 Help the children hone their mental arithmetic strategies by asking them, for example, to add ten to 40, 50, 60; add nine to 41, 51, 61; add thirteen to 16, 26, 36, and so on. This will help them develop mental pictures of patterns in addition to help them solve and check tens and units calculations.

Assessment

Child performance	Teacher action
Cannot do practical addition (and subtraction) using mathematical apparatus	Revise the concept of place value and give some practice in doing calculations to 20, before repeating the exercises above
Can use apparatus to set out tens and units	Give more opportunities in using apparatus in setting out tens and units before and during the next lesson
Speedy and confident in using apparatus and achieving answers	Move on to the next lesson

Lesson 2   ②

Key questions

Can you add these numbers together?

What is the answer to this subtraction?

These units add up to more than ten, so what shall we do now?

I cannot take eight units from two units, so what must I do?

Vocabulary

Decomposition, carrying, exchanging, tens, units.

Introduction $\boxed{10\text{min}}$

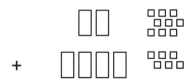 Set out in front of the children, either on the board or better still, using mathematical apparatus, an addition involving tens and units where the added units will exceed ten, for example, 29 + 46, as shown below.

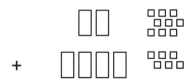

Arrange the apparatus as shown here and show the children how the calculation can be done, talking about it as you do it, thus: 'We want to add 29 and 46. Let's add the units first. Nine add six is 15. We can exchange ten of these units for one ten and place the five units in the answer. Now let's add the tens. Two tens and four tens make six tens and the one ten we have made already make seven tens. The answer is seventy-five.' Talk about and demonstrate at least two more examples. Leave the examples laid out or written on the board.

Activities $\boxed{30\text{min}}$

 Allow each group to use apparatus and set out and recap the examples done in the introduction. The groups should then set out the first three examples on **Copymaster 39**, in turn. If there are any uncertainties about what to do this is the children's chance to ask for help.

 Ask the children to complete Copymaster 39 starting with the three examples they worked through in their groups. The children can continue to use apparatus if they wish.

Closing the lesson $\boxed{15\text{min}}$

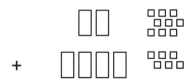 Give the children a 'Tens and unit challenge' to which they write down the answers. Here are some example questions: 54 + 17, 32 + 40: which of these has the bigger total? Write down three numbers that add to a number with six tens. What is the total of the ages of the people in your group?

Assessment

Child performance	Teacher action
Cannot work with addition (and subtraction) to 100	Revise the concept of place value and give some practice in doing calculations to 20, before repeating Lesson 1 in this theme. Repeat this lesson
Can work to 100 but makes errors	Give more practice in doing these kinds of calculations
Confident in working to 100 including 'carrying' and decomposition	Move on to the next lesson

Lesson 3   ③

Key questions

What should we do with the numbers in this story to solve it?

Vocabulary

Solve, create, problem, 'number story'.

Introduction $\boxed{15\text{min}}$

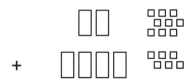 Give children in different parts of the room a street name card each. Place the 'mail' for each street in a 'sack'. The mail can have elastic bands around it with the number of letters in the bundle and the street name on the front. Hold a 'crib' sheet showing the total number of letters and number in each bundle.

Appoint a post-person who can walk around delivering the bundles to the people with the street signs, in the order you suggest. As they go, tell the class what is happening, for example: 'Delia the post person has 86 letters to deliver this morning, 27 are for Hawthorn Drive. She delivers them. Now class, how many has she still got to deliver? Next she delivers 16 to Holly Road, how many are left now?... and so on, until the sack is empty. Tell the children that this is a number story involving subtraction.

Activities

 Ask the children to work out the number story on **Copymaster 40** and then write a number story for themselves. Mathematical apparatus should be available.

Closing the lesson

Play class Bingo. Draw a grid on the board. It can be any even number of squares depending on the time available) – let us say 16 squares. Divide the class into two teams each with a team colour. Hand out to each child or pair of children in each team an answer card – there are sixteen of these (check that the teams hold matching answer cards). Place 16 calculation cards (with additions or subtractions to give the answers on the answer cards) in a hat. Pull them out one at a time and hold them up. The child with the answer calls out and a square in the grid is given their team colour. The winning team is the one with most squares on the grid.

Assessment

Child performance	Teacher action
Cannot solve and create number 'stories'	Give more practical maths activities which the children can 'talk through' in story form. Then help the children to record the stories before asking them to create some with small numbers involved
Has difficulty in solving and creating number stories	Give more practice in creating stories using small numbers at first
Can solve and create number stories	The learning targets for this theme have been met

Homework

Give each child a piece of A4 paper from which a small booklet can be made as shown below. In the booklet they can write a number story, placing one part of the story (and one mathematical operation) on each page.

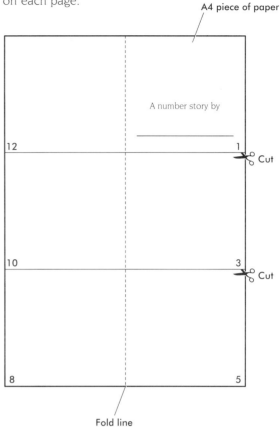

Cut where indicated and place pages in order along fold line. Number remaining blank pages in sequence. Staple or stitch together along fold line.

THEME 13

Adding and subtracting money

Learning targets

On completion of this theme the children should be able to:

1 ➡→ use the vocabulary of shopping and money

2 ➡→ recognise coins and understand equivalence

3 ➡→ add and subtract using coins

Before you start

Subject knowledge

One of the most important everyday applications of our knowledge of place value and work with numbers is in shopping, and it is, therefore, important that children understand what shopping is, how a sale is made and so on. They should also be able to work out which coins they need to create totals, and the relative 'values' of coins. Addition and subtraction of money is important to them in calculating their change and what they can afford to buy. The three lessons in Theme 13 are on money problems.

Previous knowledge required

Addition and subtraction to 100 (for Lesson 3).

Resources needed for Lesson 1

Class shop with small items on a tray 'for sale' and shopping bags and play coins, Copymaster 41, a cheque book, plastic card, and pictures or photographs of a supermarket checkout, cash machine and ordinary shop till.

Resources needed for Lesson 2

An overhead projector would be useful, the following real coins 1p, 2p, 5p, 10p, 20p, 50p and £1 and plenty of play replicas to draw around, purse outlines (see page 37) – five for each child, money spinners made up from spinner D on Copymaster 90.

Resources needed for Lesson 3

Play coins to draw around or use to help in calculating, Copymasters 42 and 43, spend and save spinners made up from spinner E on Copymaster 90.

Teaching the lessons

Lesson 1 ①

Key questions

What does 'p' stand for?

How much does this cost?

What do I need to pay the shopkeeper?

Why do I need to pay the shopkeeper?

Vocabulary

Spend, change, bill, shopping, pay, buy, sell, money.

Introduction | 10min |

▦ Talk to the children about their experiences of shopping. Make a class word list of all the important words they have used in relation to shopping. Check that they are using vocabulary like pay, price, and change appropriately.

Activities | 40min |

▦ Show the class a little shop (set up before the lesson) with small items on a tray 'for sale', and shopping bags and play coins. Explain to the children what the price of the items is and check that appropriate play coins are on offer so that the children can exchange one coin for an item in the shop. Tell the children that our coins are all pence and when we say 10p the 'p' means pence.

▨▨ Allow the children access to the class shop, for just a couple of minutes, so that each child can be shopkeeper and then customer. They can take turns while all the other children are working through the next activity.

▧ Invite the children to complete the money puzzles on **Copymaster 41**.

▦ Show the children a cheque book and plastic card and talk about what these are.

Closing the lesson | 5min |

▦ Show the children pictures or photographs of a supermarket checkout, cash machine and an ordinary shop till, and discuss with them what happens when we use these machines and what they are for.

Assessment

Child performance	Teacher action
Does not understand what happens when we shop	Allow the children to shop from you while you play the shopkeeper and explain what is happening step by step. Then allow the children to 'buy' things and act as shop-keeper, while explaining what they are doing
Can talk about shopping and carry out a shopping transaction.	Give more practice and help with recording before tackling the Copymaster again and then moving on
Can make a record of simple shopping activities	Move on to the next lesson

Lesson 2 ②

Key questions

What is this coin?

If I bought something with this what would I spend?

Vocabulary

Pence, p., match, the same as, value.

Introduction `10min`

If the overhead projector is available, lay one of each of the real coins on it, so that the children will see them as dark shapes with a distinctive outline. Ask the children if, by just looking at the shapes, they can identify them. Point out which are circular and which have a small number of sides.

Activities `40min`

Without seeing the coins invite the children to say how the coins should appear in order. Write up the order on the board as follows: 1p, 2p, 5p, 10p, 50p and £1. Discuss with the children the fact that 'p' is short for pence. Draw another pound sign. Allow the children to trace the sign several times with a finger in the air.

Give each child a piece of rough paper and invite them to draw the coins, from memory, in order of value and making the appropriate shapes.

Give each group a pile of play coins and ask the children to treat these as 'real' for this activity. Set them challenges such as: 'Show me two ways of making 2p.' '2p, 2p and 1p make 5p. What other ways are there to make 5p?'

After several challenges issued to all the class at once, ask the children, in their groups, to take turns at spinning a spinner and making up the sum spun (using more than one coin each time – except with 1p).

Give each child five purse outlines such as those shown right and ask them to draw 10p in each one, using a different set of coins each time.

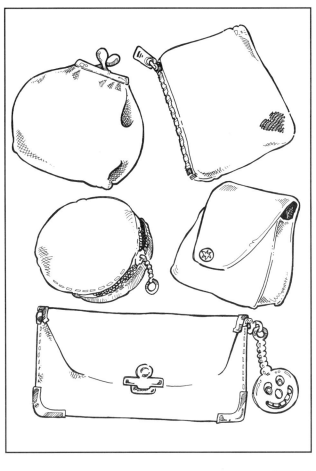

Closing the lesson `10min`

Give each pair of children a piggy bank or post box money box outline and plenty of play coins. Call out 8p, 4p and so on and ask them to assemble coins to this value on their outline.

Assessment

Child performance	Teacher action
Cannot recognise coins or understand equivalence	In a one-to-one or small group situation, allow the children to examine real coins, talk about their shapes and sizes, and look at how the values of the coins are written down. Show the children a range of ways of making up the values of each coin and then allow them to visit the class shop and 'buy' items using several coins for a transaction. Then repeat this lesson
Cannot fully understand equivalence	Show the children a range of ways of making up the values of each coin and then allow them to visit the class shop and 'buy' items using several coins for a transaction. Then repeat this lesson
Can work with coins understanding their values	Move on to the next lesson

37

Lesson 3 ③

Key questions

What is the total here?

What is left if I spend ...p?

If I give ...p to the shopkeeper for this which costs ...p, how much change will I have?

Vocabulary

Add, coins, money, price, cost, change.

Introduction `10min`

▦ Begin the lesson by giving the children money box and piggy bank outlines like those they had when closing Lesson 2. Each pair should also have a pile of play coins. Ask them to put, for example, 10p in the box and then to take the 10p, spend 2p and put what is left back in the box. Do several calculations like this, using addition and subtraction.

Activities `20min`

👤 Ask the children to complete **Copymaster 42**, drawing around the play coins they need.

Closing the lesson `20min`

▦ Using a 'spend and save' spinner made up from E on **Copymaster 90** allow the children to play the 5 game set out on **Copymaster 43**.

Assessment

Child performance	Teacher action
Cannot add and subtract using coins	Give the children revision practice of addition and subtraction and then work with coins on exchange and equivalence before repeating this lesson
Can add coin values but gets stuck on subtraction and the idea of 'change'	Give more practice including 'play shopping' and other practical experience of exchange, equivalence and giving change
Can add and subtract using coins	The learning targets for this theme have been met

Homework

Ask the children to collect price tags and shopping receipts that they can show and talk about in a class discussion.

Investigations

- Take a yellow Cuisenaire® rod and see how many ways it can be made using other rods.
- Investigate the relationships between components of Cuisenaire®. Make up some problems for others to try, using Cuisenaire® and Multilink® or Unifix®.
- Add the numbers at the corners of diagrams as shown below.

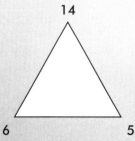

$14 + 5 = \boxed{}$

$14 + 6 = \boxed{}$

$6 + 5 = \boxed{}$

- Do more puzzles like this. Extend to shapes other than the triangle.
- Make up addition and subtraction games using two and then three dice.

Assessment

- Add ten to any number.
- Add two to any number.
- Make cards with additions or subtractions on them using a two digit and a one digit number.
- Find all the possible ways to make 15, 12 and 20.
- Call out number bonds in addition and subtraction to 20.
- Use apparatus to complete a range of addition and subtraction problems.

FRACTIONS

The children will probably have already met fractions before they start school, in the context of sharing foods or other things between themselves and other members of the family. There is a range of other everyday situations in which we use fractions. For example, we mark time and read a clock face using fractions (including 'half an hour' and 'a quarter past') and we use fraction words in talking about timing and positions in football, hockey and other games (including 'half time' and 'quarter back'). We also use fraction words and ideas in phrases for things like distance (for example, 'we are halfway there').

Children need to learn to manipulate fractions not only for these everyday events, but also for use in many of the school subjects they study, including mathematics, science, technology and music. The increased use of decimals with the adoption of the metric system has not reduced the importance of learning fractions.

Fractions are commonly viewed as parts of one whole, but this is only one of the contexts for use. We also need to give children experience of fractions of numbers of objects. It is the case that fractions are used as a way of describing a quantity – 'that is half of a cake' and as an expression of intention or an instruction – 'cut this is in half'. Children need to be taught both of these kinds of use.

As the children progress it is vital that they understand equivalent fractions as this is the basis on which their ability to manipulate fractions will be built. Equivalent fraction work can start very early on with, for example, two quarters making a half.

THEME 14 | Half

Learning targets

On completion of this theme the children should be able to:

1 ➤➤ identify a half of a single whole

2 ➤➤ calculate a half of a number of objects and half of a number

3 ➤➤ use the word and symbol for half

Before you start

Subject knowledge

There are two key elements that the children should be helped to grasp in relation to the concept of half. The first is the idea that if a single whole is cut into two equal parts, each part is called a half. (This makes nonsense of the expression 'Give me the bigger half!'). The second is that a group of objects can also be split into two equal sets, and we say each set is a half of the original set of objects or number.

Previous knowledge required

Experience in everyday life and in Home Corner play of sharing between two. Equipment sharing when working in pairs.

Resources needed for Lesson 1

Make, from card or play dough, a number of items

in halves that can be fitted together and taken apart readily: these should be replicas of everyday food items like a cake, a pizza, or an apple; a blackboard or large sheets of paper on which both teacher and children can write; Copymaster 44; sugar paper shapes – circles, equilateral triangles and rectangles (two of each for every child); scissors; glue and large sheets of paper to glue shapes onto; clock face.

Resources needed for Lesson 2

Small even numbers of pencils, crayons, postcards, badges, books and other items from around the classroom; plastic replica coins; Centicubes® or other construction sets that build into towers.

Resources needed for Lesson 3

Interactive display on 'Half' which children can view and 'work on'; Copymaster 45.

Teaching the lessons

Lesson 1 ①

Key questions

Are halves always exactly the same?

Does it matter which half you have?

Vocabulary

Whole one, half, halve, fraction.

Introduction 15min

▦ Ask the children about their own experiences of 'sharing'. Tell the children that when we share something out we are doing mathematics. Show the children one of the play items. Separate the pieces and give each to a child. Say that each is having a half share. Tell the children that each piece is called a half. A part of a whole one like this is a fraction. Repeat the sharing with the other home made items amongst different children. Allow several children it turn to act as 'sharer' and as 'teacher'.

Activities 35min

👤 Ask the children to complete **Copymaster 44**.

▦ Call the children together and repeat the sharing

demonstrations using the play items. Then draw a whole circle on the board or a large sheet of paper and invite a child to draw a line cutting the shape into two halves. Draw a second circle and ask a child to cut the shape in half using a line in a different direction. Try this several times. Then draw an equilateral triangle on the board, and show how this can be cut in half. Draw two more triangles like this and invite a child to cut each in half, drawing the cutting line in a different direction.

👤 Give each child two of each of the following cut from sugar paper: a circle, an equilateral triangle and a rectangle. Ask the children to fold one of each of these shapes in half, and cut along the fold. They should then glue a whole shape and alongside it half this shape, on a large sheet of paper.

Closing the lesson 10min

▦ Show the children a clock face and ask children in turn to set the clock at 'half past'. Point out that we say 'half past', because the minute hand has moved half way around the clock.

Assessment

Child performance	Teacher action
Cannot identify halves or share into halves	Allow children directed play with the play items and in home corner
Can recognise and name half of a whole one	Go on to the next lesson
Uses fraction vocabulary with confidence	Go on to the next lesson

Lesson 2 ②

Key questions

What is half of 2, 4, 6, etc?

What do we mean by 'fair shares'?

Vocabulary

Share, half price, half size.

Introduction 15 min

 Do some sharing-between-two demonstrations, this time using pencils and other collections of items. Hand out one at a time, saying: 'one for Debbie and one for Malik, one for Debbie and one for Malik', and so on. Check that the children understand that the process of halving like this is similar to sharing a cake. (Each child has half a cake, half a box of pencils etc.) Work on halving all even numbers up to 20.

Show the children a 10p coin and ask 'If something at this price was sold at half price, how much would it cost?' Repeat this with other prices (using even numbers) up to 20p.

Activities 25 min

 Using the play coins ask the children to lay out alongside each other 2p, 4p, 6p and so on up to 20p and half of these amounts.

Ask the children to make Centicube® or other construction towers, up to 20 and half size ones to set alongside. They should then view each group's constructions and say how many there are in the whole tower and the the half-sized tower.

Closing the lesson 10 min

Give the children some quick-fire questions on halving numbers and prices up to 20p.

Assessment

Child performance	Teacher action
Cannot find half of a group of objects	Give more opportunities for practical work as in Lessons 1 and 2
Can halve using real objects but not small numbers	Go on to the next lesson
Can halve numbers with confidence	Go on to the next lesson

Lesson 3

Key questions

What does this word say?

What is this the symbol for?

Can you match this to its half?

Vocabulary

Symbol, half term, half way, half time.

Introduction 5 min

Ask the children to think of all times we use 'half' when we talk. Some examples to include are half term, half way and half time.

Activities 45 min

Teach the children the spelling of 'half' and 'halve' and the symbol for $\frac{1}{2}$, using the words and symbols on the board or on large cards.

Give the children the opportunity to record the word and symbol for half on **Copymaster 45**.

Provide an interactive display on halves and invite children to place 'wholes' and halves alongside one another. All the children can look on while one child has a go at a task. The display can then be left up for all the children to look at.

Closing the lesson 5 min

If the children have worked on division, assure them that halving is the same as dividing by two. Look with the children at the idea that half an odd number is always a whole number and a half, for example, half of 3 is $1\frac{1}{2}$).

Assessment

Child performance	Teacher action
Unsure of half in any of a range of contexts	Recap Lessons 1 and 2 using more practical activities
Understands the concept but not sure of the word or symbol for half	Offer more practice in writing the word and symbol for half
Is confident with a half and uses symbol and word correctly	Move on to the next theme

Homework

Invite the children to make a note of 'Half in my Saturday' to show the contexts in which half is important to them. The record could be a series of pictures showing, for example, half shares of the cereal left in the box at breakfast, reading half a book, eating half an apple, playing football and scoring near half time. Ask the children to write down a list of the numbers 1 to 20 and alongside each what half that number is. This gives practice in writing the symbol for half.

THEME 15 | Quarter

Learning targets

On completion of this theme the children should be able to:

1 ➡➤ identify a quarter of a single whole
2 ➡➤ calculate a quarter of a number of objects and a quarter of a number
3 ➡➤ use the word and symbol for a quarter and recognise three-quarters

Before you start

Subject knowledge

The children should find the ideas here plain sailing after their work on a half. The main elements include the fact that if a single whole one is cut into four equal parts each part is called a quarter, and when a group of objects can be placed in four equal sets each set is a quarter of the original set of objects.

Previous knowledge required

Half and halving; experience of sharing between four.

Resources needed for Lesson 1

Some fruits: apples, bananas, pears and oranges (include enough for each child to have a piece) and a knife and board on which to cut them. Make, from card or play dough, a number of items in quarters that can be fitted together and taken apart readily: these should be replicas of everyday food items like cakes; Copymaster 46; a range of art materials, (enough for each child in the class to work with) including paints, chalks, felt-tipped pens and charcoal; overalls; paper.

Resources needed for Lesson 2

Marbles, pencils, blocks, books and other items which can be shared out (each group will need 20 of each of the sharing item; Copymaster 47.

Resources needed for Lesson 3

Flashcards each with one of the following on it (make several of each): the word 'quarter', the symbol for a quarter, the word 'three-quarters', and the symbol for three-quarters; Copymaster 48.

Teaching the lessons

Lesson 1 ①

Key questions

How much of the cake/pizza has Lisa got?
What are these fractions called/
Does it matter which piece you have?

Vocabulary

Whole, share, quarter.

Introduction | 10 min |

▓ Name each fruit in turn and carefully cut it into four equal pieces, using a clean knife and board. Explain what you are doing and point out that if a whole is cut into four equal parts, each part is called a quarter. Push the pieces back together to show that four quarters make a whole one. Allow each child to have a quarter of a fruit to eat. Store the knife in a safe place.

Activities | 35 min |

▣ Ask the children to complete **Copymaster 46**.

▓ Show the children the play dough food items. Share each out in turn, giving a child each of the quarters. Ask them questions such as 'What is the size of your share?'; 'How many people have a piece?'; 'What has the pizza/cake been cut into?' Allow children in turn to act as the teacher and do the sharing out.

⦿ Give each group of four children a large sheet of paper folded into quarters and opened out again. They can work together to make a composite picture, where each child completes one section or quarter of the whole. Different groups can use use different media so the whole class completes this task at the same time. The resulting pictures can be added to a 'Quarter' display.

Closing the lesson | 10 min |

▓ Hold up each piece of the play dough pizza separately and ask a child to name the fraction. All the pieces can be pushed together and a child asked to say how many quarters.

Assessment

Child performance	Teacher action
Cannot recognise or name a quarter of a whole	More practical sharing play using whole items cut into four equal parts
Uses quarter but lacks confidence	Give more practice in naming fractions
Confident in using quarter of one whole	Move on to the next lesson

Lesson 2 ②

Key questions

What is a quarter of four? eight? 12? 16? 20?

What fraction of eight is two?

Of what number is four a quarter?

Vocabulary

Share, divide, cut, group, set, quarter.

Introduction `10min`

From a bag of marbles take out four and share them between four children. Ask the children what the starting number was, and what fraction of that number each child has. Repeat this activity with other children, using eight, 12, 16 and 20 marbles. Allow children to repeat this activity, acting as teacher.

Activities `35min`

Give each workgroup 20 pencils, blocks or other items to practise sharing with. Allow the group to take turns setting out quarter shares of four, eight, 12, 16 and 20. Every child in the group should have several goes. Visit each group and check the work.

Ask the children to record some work on **Copymaster 47**.

Show the children the clock face. Point out the quarter hours and why we say 'quarter past' and 'quarter to (the hour)'. Set the clock at quarter to or past several times and ask what the time is.

Closing the lesson `10min`

Use quick-fire questioning to ask children to name a quarter of a number and then say the answer to 'What is … the quarter of?'

Assessment

Child performance	Teacher action
Cannot find a quarter of a set of objects, or share by four	Give more practical sharing practice using classroom equipment
Can find a quarter of a set of objects	Move on to the next lesson giving plenty of mental challenges
Can find a quarter of a set of objects or a number	Move on to the next lesson

Lesson 3 ③

Key questions

What does this word say?

What is this the symbol for?

Vocabulary

Quarter, $\frac{1}{4}$, three-quarters.

Introduction `10min`

Remind the children of the contexts in which we use a quarter (a fraction of a whole one or of a set of objects). Show the children a flashcard with the word 'quarter' on it. Read it aloud with them. Write the word on the blackboard and invite several children in turn to the blackboard to copy the word. Place a flashcard alongside a quarter of a set of objects.

Activities `35min`

Ask the children to complete the first part of **Copymaster 48**.

Now show the children the flashcard with the symbol for a quarter on it. Repeat the activities done in the introduction, but this time using the symbol.

Allow each workgroup 20 items to place in groups and a flashcard for the word and the symbol for a quarter. Ask them to allow each child the chance to share the things into four groups and assign the two flashcards to a quarter.

Ask the children to finish their work on Copymaster 48.

Arrange one set of 20 items into quarters. Then push two groups together and ask what size is each share. Then push another quarter share into this pile and say that we call this fraction three-quarters. Show the children the flashcards for the word and symbol for three-quarters.

Closing the lesson `10min`

Using one of the play dough items and the flashcards, allow children to take turns at holding up a quarter, or three-quarters of the play pizza/cake while another holds up the word and a third holds up the symbol. The rest of the class can call out what is correct. Finally hold up a whole item and an additional quarter and confirm that the children can say this is one and a quarter.

Assessment

Child performance	Teacher action
Cannot read and write the words and symbols	Do more practical and oral work before repeating this lesson
Can read and write the words and symbols	Move on to the next lesson
Confident in using these words and symbols and beginning to explore other sizes of fraction	Move on to the next lesson

Homework

Give each child a circle of white paper to fold in half and then quarters and pretend it is a pizza or chapatti. They can draw on each quarter a different favourite topping or spicy dish.

Ask the children to see if they can find out about quarter finals, quarterly magazines, and quartets.

43

The number line

Learning targets

On completion of this theme the children should be able to:

1 ➡ show that they know that a number line is continuous

2 ➡ find halves and quarters on a number line

3 ➡ use a number line to do additions and subtractions involving halves

Before you start

Subject knowledge

The most important concept related to the number line is that it is continuous and that in between numbers on the line there are points which can be identified as fractions or decimal fractions. In these lessons the focus will be on halves and quarters so that the children can place these on their own mental number line.

Previous knowledge required

Numbers to 20, halves, quarters.

Resources needed for Lesson 1

A continuous large scale number line stuck to the classroom floor and covered in cover film to prevent scuffing. (Note that it should run from zero to 20, with the points on the line – not the spaces between – marked with the numerals and that each point should be equidistant from the next, and between them a mark should appear for each quarter and half, as shown below), prepared desk-sized number lines that are similar to the floor line (one for each pair of children); counters; 30cm measuring rules.

Resources needed for Lesson 2

As Lesson 1, Copymaster 49; a number of cards (around 40) each with a number or a mixed fraction on it below 20, suitable for placing on the floor number line; a set of small cards, made up using Copymaster 91, for each pair of children.

Resources needed for Lesson 3

As Lesson 1, Copymaster 50.

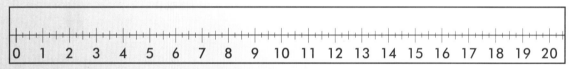

0 1 2 3 4 5 6 7 8 9 10 11 12 13 14 15 16 17 18 19 20

Note that the line begins at 0 but goes on beyond 20 to show it could continue

Teaching the lessons

Lesson 1 ①

Key questions

Which number comes next?

What comes before this number?

What comes between say three and five?

Vocabulary

Number line, numeral, count.

Introduction [15min]

▨ Using the floor number line, point out to the children the following features: the line begins at zero; this line ends at 20, but it could go on above 20; and all the numbers are spaced equally along the line.

Invite each of a number of children to stand on the line and follow challenges such as to stand on six; stand on the number between 10 and 12; stand on one less than 16; stand on one more than three; stand on two less than 20.

Activities [30min]

▨▨ Give each pair of children a desk number line and two counters. Call out some challenges and then ask a pair each time for their answer, against which all the other children can check what they have done. Some examples are to put their counters on seven and seventeen; one more than six and three less than 12; the highest number with one ten in it and the highest number with only units.

▨ Using the floor number line ask one child from each pair in turn to set challenges for his or her partner, while the class look on.

Closing the lesson [10min]

▨ Pass around some 30cm rules and allow the children to see that these tools are a kind of number line where the space between the numbers has been set at 1cm. Note that zero does not appear but the mark for it is there. We can measure a whole range of things using a cm number line which can be as long as required.

Assessment

Child performance	Teacher action
Has no concept of a continuous number line	Allow more practical experience with both floor and desk number lines
Can show numbers on the line but is slow or underconfident	Give the children some mental challenges using the number line and then move on to next lesson
Is speedy and accurate at finding numbers on the number line.	Move on to the next lesson

Lesson 2 ②

Key questions

Where is $3\frac{1}{4}$?

Can you show me $6\frac{1}{2}$, $17\frac{3}{4}$ … ?

Vocabulary

Number line. half, quarter.

Introduction 15 min

▦ Using the floor number line and the cards with numbers and mixed fractions on them, ask children in turn to place the cards on the line where they think they go. The cards may say, for example, $4\frac{1}{2}$, $15\frac{3}{4}$, 17, $9\frac{1}{4}$ etc.

Activities 30 min

👥 Give the children a desk number line and a set of cards made up from **Copymaster 91**. Ask them to place the cards in a pile face down on the desk. They can then take turns at turning them up and saying where they appear on the number line. Look at the work the children are doing, and invite them to ask you about any challenge that they are not sure about.

👤 Invite the children to complete **Copymaster 49**.

Closing the lesson 10 min

▦ Give the children a number line test. Use a pointer to indicate places on the floor number line and ask them to write the number or mixed fraction pointed at on a piece of paper. It should be possible to fit in ten such challenges in ten minutes and the outcomes can be used as part of the assessment.

Assessment

Child performance	Teacher action
Not sure about where halves and quarters appear on a number line	Give more practical work using a number line
Can place halves and quarters on a line but recording has errors	Give some more challenges involving recording on and about number lines
Can competently place and record fractions on a number line	Go on to the next lesson

Lesson 3 ③

Key questions

What is one more than $2\frac{1}{2}$?

What is a half less than $17\frac{1}{2}$?

What is 16 subtract $2\frac{1}{2}$ on the number line?

Vocabulary

Number line, less than, more than, add, subtract, minus, difference.

Introduction 10 min

▦ Using the floor number line show the children how to add on half to a number. Give them challenges in quick-fire succession. For example, what is ten add a half? 14 add a half? six add a half? Then show them what happens when half is added to a half, as in $4\frac{1}{2}$ add a half. Show them on the number line where to stand and where the addition of a half takes you. Allow several children to have goes at standing on the line and stepping forward a half.

Activities 30 min

👤 Give the children **Copymaster 50** to work on.

▦ Have another look at the floor number line, but this time show the children what happens in subtraction of half.

⚫⚫ In their workgroups allow the children time to work out a series of challenges involving the number line and half (say six challenges, which they can write down on rough paper).

Closing the lesson 15 min

▦ Take a challenge from each of the workgroups in turn, and allow children from another group to show how to work it out. Then take another from each of the lists, until the lesson finishes. Remaining challenges can be photocopied for the children to try as homework.

Assessment

Child performance	Teacher action
Cannot do addition and subtraction of half using the line	Give more practice using the floor and desk top number line
Uses the number line but cannot work at speed	Give an assignment using the line and recording answers in a time limit
Does challenges quickly and competently	Move on to another theme

Homework

Give the children the challenges remaining at the end of Lesson 3. Allow them to take home a strip of cm squared paper and create a number line.

Investigations

- Using Cuisenaire® apparatus invite the children to make $\frac{1}{2}$ of one rod, $\frac{1}{4}$ of another.
- Measure the lengths of pencils, the 'weight' of small bags of pasta, rice and lentils, and the volumes of containers like mugs and plastic pots using non-standard measures. Then work out half lengths, half weights and volume when half filled.
- Play with plane mirrors to halve pictures, make another half, compare halves.
- Make patterns involving halves and quarters by colouring shapes.
- Cut shapes into halves and quarters and then remake the shapes.
- Make a record of the fraction of a family-sized pizza eaten by each person around the table.
- Make a decorative number line with numbers from zero to ten and all the halves also (for example, $\frac{1}{2}$, $1\frac{1}{2}$, $2\frac{1}{2}$,)

Assessment

- Give children a list of the numbers 1 to 5 and ask them to list the numbers of which each of these numbers is half, and the numbers of which they are a quarter.
- Ask the children to draw pictures with half or a quarter missing, for example half a full moon, half a wheel, half a book, half a flower, a quarter of a face mask or a quarter of a banana.
- Give the children a sheet with drawings of pencils on it. All the pencils should be the same length. Ask the children to mark in on different pencils one half, two quarters, three quarters.
- Set out a little shop counter and give each item a price tag. Invite the children to say or write what the prices would be if there was a half price sale. How much would each item cost if we could buy four for the price of one?

MULTIPLICATION AND DIVISION

Multiplication is usually first experienced in school in the context of the repeated addition of equal groups. For example, we may set out four groups of three small toys and ask a child how many there are altogether. The child should establish that the groups are all of equal size, and all '3s' and then by counting in 3s (adding $3 + 3 + 3 + 3$) find a total. If we say 'Three children have 2 pencils each; how many pencils are there altogether?', this can be written as $2 + 2 + 2 = 3$ lots of $2 = 3$ x 2. Young children can, in this way make mathematical statements about real objects. Clearly an array of '3 twos' can also be seen as '2 threes' and beyond their infant education children should be introduced to the concepts of multiplier and multiplicand. Repeated addition is one of the methods we can place in children's repertoires. They will need others, for example, when multiplying fractions like this: $\frac{1}{2}$ x $\frac{1}{2}$, the product is not 1 but a quarter.

Through their work on multiplications the children can come to have an understanding of the commutative and distributive laws. The former is shown here: 3 x $2 = 2$ x 3. The latter law is demonstrated by this statement: 5 x $6 = (3$ x $6) + (2$ x $6)$. Children who understand the commutative law will know that it is possible to change the order of the numbers in a multiplication, taking the larger number first, in order to make the calculation easier to do, and that this will not affect the outcome. A knowledge of the distributive law helps children's mathematical skills because, if we

know, for example, the product of 5 x 3, the product of 6 x 3 can be derived from those of 5 x 3 and 1 x 3.

There is a third law that children may not meet in their infant years, but which should be available, and that is the associative law. For example: 3 x 2 x $5 = (3$ x $2)$ x $5 = 3$ x $(2$ x $5)$

A knowledge of the products of multiplications (times tables) is important, but learning by chanting is only one of the ways of working on them. What is crucial is the quick recall of multiplication products without having to chant the whole table through.

Division can be seen as containing two important ideas. These are sharing and grouping. In sharing we start with the number of sets we have to divide things into and work out the number in each set. For example, there are 4 children (number of sets) and 12 sweets; how many each? When grouping we know how many will appear in each set but wish to know how many of these sets we can make. Thus, for example, if there are 15 pencils and we wish each person to have 5, how many people have a share?

Division is neither commutative nor associative, so the children need to know that we cannot order the figures so as to make the calculation easier to do. Division is, however, the inverse of multiplication, and this idea not only helps in doing divisions, but also when they are confident in using these operations, allows the children to check their work.

THEME 17

Introducing multiplication

Learning targets

On completion of this theme the children should be able to:

1 ➤➤ do repeated addition and work with 'lots of' 2, 3 etc.

2 ➤➤ record multiplications using the multiplication sign

3 ➤➤ solve multiply puzzles

Before you start

Subject knowledge

This theme concerns one of the milestone steps in children's education about manipulating numbers. Multiplication is repeated addition and that is where the children should begin. This theme should set the scene for the times tables, for which there are sample lessons in the next theme.

Previous knowledge required

Addition (to at least 20, but preferably beyond), counting patterns of 2, 5 and 10

Resources needed for Lesson 1

A large collection of objects that can be used for counting (about twenty of each item) such as soft toys, wooden blocks, shells, pencils, crayons; pictures of objects (and words), such as those shown below, mounted on card which can be photocopied several times and cut out to be used in activities and games; Copymaster 51.

Resources needed for Lesson 2

Individual number lines to 20 made up from Copymaster 94; several sets of flashcards with numerals 1 to 5 on them, and flashcards with the words 'multiply by', 'times' and equals on them; cards with the equals and multiplication signs on them; Copymaster 52.

Resources needed for Lesson 3

Painting table set up with paper, paints and brushes; game boards made up from Copymaster 54 (enough for each pair of children in the class) and spinners made from Copymaster 90; Copymaster 53.

two wheels

three apples

four legs

five fingers

six sides

seven stars

Teaching the lessons

Lesson 1 ①

Key questions

Can you add two more?

How many lots of three here?

What do three lots of four make?

Vocabulary

Add, addition, repeated, 'lots of'.

Introduction 15min

▦ Show the children a collection of toys or counting blocks. Set out two objects apart from the pile. Announce that this is 'one lot of two'. Set up another two, and call this pattern 'two lots of two'. Ask the children what the total number of objects is. Then say 'So two lots of two is four'. Arrange more lots of two, up to five lots.

Then repeat this activity, this time using 'lots of' three and using children themselves to place in groups of three.

Activities 30min

⚫⚫ Write, on the blackboard, a list of challenges for which the children could find the total, such as five lots of three, four lots of two, two lots of five, one lot of four, three lots of three. Ask each group to set these out and work out the totals. Visit each group and give them quick-fire questions about the totals and the patterns they have made. Ask them to go through the pattern of challenges several times, allowing everyone several different goes.

👤 Ask the children to do the 'lots of' calculations on **Copymaster 51**.

Closing the lesson 10min

▦ Using the pictures copied several times and mounted on card (see 'Resources'), play 'Lots of' with the class. This game can be varied so that groups can play one another or it can be played as a class thus: ask a child to stand at the front and lay out all the cards face up on the teacher's table. Then set a challenge, for example, 'five lots of four' or simply 'five fours', and the child has to collect and hold up the appropriate cards, as shown below:

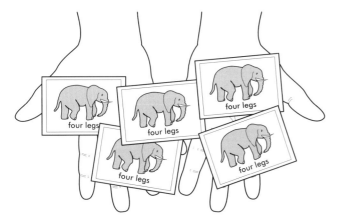

The class can then call out the total. Allow the child to have several goes and then ask another child to take their place. This time, announce a total, for example 'six', and the child should hold up two lots of three or three lots of two, and the class can look at and call out what is being held up.

Assessment

Child performance	Teacher action
Cannot do repeated addition	Give the children practical help in setting out and adding 2 + 2 + 2 etc. using apparatus. Also ask them to say aloud the numbers in 'counting in twos', 'counting in fives' and 'counting in tens' patterns
Cannot work with 'lots of' 2, 3 etc.	Give the child more practice in using 'lots of' with activities like those used in the lesson
Can work with 'lots of'	Move on to the next lesson

Lesson 2 ②

Key questions

What is two multiplied by four? What is four multiplied by two?

What is the product here?

What are two twos?

What is two times three?

Vocabulary

Multiply, multiplied by, multiplication, times, product.

Introduction
10 min

Draw a 'lots of' problem on the board as shown above right. Explain that instead of 'lots of' we can say 'times' and this is another way of saying 'multiplied

by'. Add to the example on the board, like this:

3	lots of	2	makes	6
2	+ 2 +	2	=	6
3	multiplied by	2	=	6
3	times	2	=	6
3	✗	2	=	6

Work through at least two more examples in the same way.

Activities
35 min

Allow the children to set out some mathematical apparatus in a 'lots of' calculation (where the total does not exceed 20). Ask them to set out the numeral and sign flashcards to show a multiplication to match the array of apparatus. Everyone in the group should have time to set out a different calculation.

Give each child a number line to 20. Draw a number line on the board. Show the children how one can demonstrate 'lots of' or 'times' two by jumping along the line as shown here:

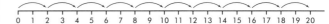

Give the whole class more multiplications to 'act out' along the line. Examples should include all the appropriate vocabulary, as in the following: what is three times two?; multiply four by three; what is the product of five times two?; how many times two is ten?

Ask the children to do the work on **Copymaster 52** using their number line or mathematical apparatus if they wish.

Closing the lesson
5 min

Hold up the multiply and equals sign flashcards and ask the children what they mean. Point out again to the children that multiplication is like adding again and again (repeated addition). Give the children multiplications like this: 4 x 3, 3 x 4, 2 x 1, 1 x 2, so that they can see that the product of a multiplication is the same, even if the multiplier and multiplicand are reversed.

Assessment

Child performance	Teacher action
Does not yet demonstrate an understanding of multiplication	Give the children practice in repeated addition as in Lesson 1 and then allow plenty of practice in the activities like those in this lesson
Cannot record multiplications using the multiplication sign	Allow the children to use flashcards with the words and signs for multiply by and equals on them for the calculations they do in class. Give more practice of the kind found on Copymaster 52

| Understands and records multiplication | Move on to the next lesson |

 Lesson 3   ③

Key questions

What is the product here?

Can you put in the missing numbers here?

Vocabulary

Multiply, multiplication.

Introduction   10 min

 Show the children a set of multiplications with missing numbers in them on the board. Here is one such example:

$$\Box \;\text{✖}\; 2 = 8$$

$$6 \;\text{✖}\; \Box = 6$$

Activities   35 min

 Ask the children to complete **Copymaster 53**.

 Allow some of the class to do this activity while some do the next, and then swop about. Give the children game boards made up from **Copymaster 54** and a dice (with faces saying one to four and an extra two and three) as shown below.

Also give the children a spinner (one to four and two and three repeated in the remaining spaces, as shown on spinner C on **Copymaster 90**) and playing counters, so that they can play the game.

 At the painting table set up with paper, paints and brushes, invite the children to work together in creating a painting where there are hidden 'two times two' cherries or 'three times two' buses, or other objects of their choice. These can be displayed along the classroom wall, and classmates can see if they can spot the 'hidden' multiplication.

Closing the lesson   10 min

Using the dice and spinner from the board game invite two children to spin and throw them and then call out the resulting multiplication, to which the class should give the answer.

Assessment

Child performance	Teacher action
Cannot solve multiply puzzles	Give more practice at the kinds of activities done in Lessons 2 and 3 of this theme
Can solve some multiplication puzzles but not yet confident	Give more practice in game playing and in using missing numbers in multiplications
Confident with the operation of multiplication	The learning targets for this theme have been met

Homework

Allow the children to take home Copymaster 54 and make up the game to play with family or friends.

THEME 18

2, 5 and 10 times tables

Learning targets

On completion of this theme the children should be able to:

1 ➠ recall and use the products in the two times table
2 ➠ show they know the five times table
3 ➠ use the two, five and ten times tables

Before you start

Subject knowledge

Times tables have always been seen by adults as an essential part of school arithmetic. There have been times in history when children have learned them by rote, and chanted them off, without really understanding how numbers are operated on to achieve a multiplication. We are not advocating rote learning, but instant recall of multiplication facts is useful, both in mathematics and in everyday life, and times tables can be a good device for remembering them.

Previous knowledge required

The experience of counting in twos, fives and tens would obviously be useful.

Resources needed for Lesson 1

24 coloured beads, 24 books, half-centimetre squared paper (Copymaster 93), Copymaster 55.

Resources needed for Lesson 2

Number lines to 50 made up from Copymaster 94; Times Five game cards made from Copymaster 57; Copymaster 56.

Resources needed for Lesson 3

Copymaster 58, flashcards – each with a product in the two, five or ten times tables on it.

Teaching the lessons

Lesson 1 ❶

Key questions

What are two twos?
Say, for me, your two times table.
How many times two is twelve?

Vocabulary

Times table.

Introduction [10 min]

▦ Lay out 24 coloured beads in twos and count them in twos. Begin again saying 'One times two is two, two times two is four' etc. Begin again and say 'Once two is two, two twos are four, three twos are six' etc. Now lay out 24 books in twos and repeat the activities asking the children to join in.

Activities [30 min]

👤 Give each child a piece of half-centimetre squared paper (**Copymaster 93**) and invite them to create a staircase of the products when we say 'times two'.

▦ Write out the two times table vertically on the board. Remind the children that a mathematical table is information presented in a clear and orderly way. Ask them to say it aloud as 'no twos are nought, once two is two, two twos are four' and so on.

👤 Ask the children to complete **Copymaster 55**.

Closing the lesson [5 min]

▦ Give the children quick-fire questions about the products in the two times table. Try some tricky questions such as 'How many products have either 2 tens or two units?' (5) or 'How many products have 4 units?' (3).

Assessment

Child performance	Teacher action
Cannot say the two times table or count in twos	Give practical and pattern-making activities involving counting in twos
Recalls and uses products in the two times table, but needs to do repeated addition to find them	Work on activities like those in this lesson, until the children can respond quicker to challenges about the two times table
Knows and uses the two times table	Move on to the next lesson

Lesson 2 ❷

Key questions

What are six fives?
What is the product of eight multiplied by five?

Vocabulary

Times table, multiplied by.

Introduction   `10 min`

 Ask five children to take off their shoes and socks and stand at the front of the class. They hold up their hands, and the class counts fingers in tens to 50. A similar count can be done using toes. Recite the five times table, while pointing to fingers or toes.

Activities   `35 min`

 Ask the children to try **Copymaster 56**.

 Give each child a number line to 50 made up from **Copymaster 94**. Invite them to say the five times table in unison while jumping in fives along the number line.

Give the children a set of Times Five game cards made from **Copymaster 57**. They can turn them all over and take turns at turning up two in an effort to find the pairs.

Closing the lesson   `5 min`

Write 0 x 5 = 0 on the board. Invite a child to write the next line of the five times table, then another child until it is complete. The class can then read it out together.

Assessment

Child performance	Teacher action
Does not know the five times table	Give the children more practical activities, in counting in fives. Use the number line to practice repeated addition. Try learning one product a day, completing the table on a special chart in twelve days (0 x 5 being written at the start)
Knows the table but finds it difficult to transfer this knowledge to new situations	Try giving the children a different challenge about the five times table every day, until they become adept at solving them
Confident with the five times table	Move on to the next lesson

Lesson 3   ③

Key questions

What are the products of the ten times table?

What are five tens?

What are ten fives?

What are two times five times ten?

Which products in the two times table are also in the fives and tens?

Vocabulary

Times table, product.

Introduction   `10 min`

Invite the children to count in tens from nought to

100. Point out that these are the products of the ten times table. Let the class say the ten times table aloud.

Activities   `30 min`

 Ask the children to tackle **Copymaster 58**.

Write, on the board, a list of the products of the two, five and ten times tables. Now write the last digit of the products in the two times table in a circle as shown below.

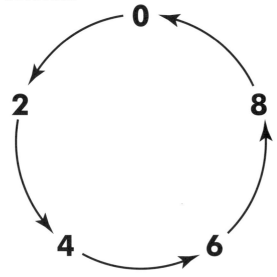

The children should note that the last digit pattern is preserved, even beyond twelve times two. Ask individual children to detect and draw the pattern for the five times table.

Closing the lesson   `10 min`

 Hold up flashcards with products from the two, five and ten times tables on them. Invite the children to put their left hand up if it is in the two times table, their right hand if it is in the five times table and one leg if it is in the ten times table.

Assessment

Child performance	Teacher action
Cannot use the two, five and ten times tables	Over several short sessions count in twos, record these as repeated additions, then multiplications and finally put them into a table. Repeat this process for 5 x and 10 x
Knows some of the multiplications but cannot apply the knowledge	Rehearse the tables again with the children and then give a few short puzzles each day until the children have memorised these multiplication facts
Can use the two, five and ten times tables	The learning targets for this theme have been met

Homework

The children can make a 2 x, 5 x and 10 x chart to stick on the fridge at home, to remind them of what they have learned.

Multiplications up to 5 x 5

Learning targets

On completion of this theme the children should be able to:

1 ➨→ recall or compute three and four times tables at least up to five times three and five times four
2 ➨→ complete multiplication squares
3 ➨→ show they know all multiplications to 5 x 5

Before you start

Subject knowledge

The purpose here is to begin to 'fill in' the children's knowledge of multiplications giving products up to 25. At the end of this theme, if they have had appropriate earlier experiences, they should have no difficulty with these first multiplications.

Previous knowledge required

A working knowledge of the two and five times tables is assumed, and these are given less emphasis here.

Resources needed for Lesson 1

Copymasters 59 and 60.

Resources needed for Lesson 2

Copymaster 61, dice with faces marked zero to five.

Resources needed for Lesson 3

Two centimetre-squared paper.

Teaching the lessons

Lesson 1 ①

Key questions

What is the answer to three times four?

What comes next after 16 in the four times table?

Vocabulary

Multiply, multiplication, multiples, product.

Introduction `15min`

Ask the children to recite their two times table, and then their five times table. Tell them that some of the multiples in the three and four times tables are the focus of this lesson.

As a reminder of multiplication as repeated addition, set out an array of five groups of three objects and five groups of four objects. Ask a volunteer child to show and compute three lots of three, four fours etc. while the class look on.

Activities `30min`

👤 Invite the children to complete **Copymaster 59**.

👥 Give the children a copy of **Copymaster 60** which has been stuck onto card. They can, with help if necessary, cut out the base boards and the multiply cards. The children should turn over all the multiply cards and arrange them in a pile. They take turns to pick a card from the top of the pile and place it face up. The first to say the product can see if the product appears on their card. If so they cover the product on the base board. The winner is the first to fill their board. There may be time to play the game twice, having shuffled the cards.

Closing the lesson `5min`

🏁 Think of a number. Say to the children, 'See if you can identify this number – it is a product in the two times table. It also appears in the four times table.' (It could be 4, 8, or if the children go further than five times it could be 12, 16, or 20.) Try more challenges like this.

Assessment

Child performance	Teacher action
Cannot recall or compute three and four times tables at least up to five times three and five times four	Give plenty of practical activity including 'lots of' and mental multiplication games
Can compute these multiplications but has not memorised them yet	Give mental multiplications every day until these facts are memorised
Recalls these multiplication facts with ease	Move on to the next lesson

Lesson 2 ②

Key questions

What goes here?

What is the missing product?

Vocabulary

Multiplication.

Introduction ⌗ |10min|

▦ Draw a grid for a two by two multiplication square on the board. Show the children how they can multiply the numbers as shown below.

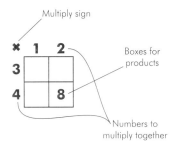

Multiply sign

Boxes for products

Numbers to multiply together

✗	1	2
3	3	6
4	4	8

Activities |30min|

👤 Invite the children to complete **Copymaster 61**.

👥 Using a dice and some rough paper the children can draw multiplication squares and take turns at throwing the dice to obtain the numbers to use for the square. They can then work out the products and fill them in. The next square they make can be swopped with that devised by a neighbouring pair of children, so that it can be solved.

Closing the lesson |10min|

👤 Draw a three by three multiplication square on the board, as shown below. Invite the children to write down the numbers missing.

✗	0	2	4
3	0		12
2		4	
1	0		

Assessment

Child performance	Teacher action
Cannot complete multiplication squares	Help the children to master conventionally presented multiplications (say the 2 x and 3 x table up to 5 x 2 and 5 x 3). Then draw a square, writing out the multiplications that emerge from it and linking them to the appropriate line in the square. Lesson 2 can then be repeated
Can complete multiplication squares but lacks confidence	Try more examples of multiplication squares, working through some together

Completes and constructs multiplication squares with confidence	Move on to the next lesson

Lesson 3 ③

Key questions

What is the product here in the grid?

Can you see a pattern of products, which cuts the grid in two halves?

Vocabulary

Multiplication square.

Introduction |5min|

▦ Remind the children of what a multiplication square looks like.

Activities |35min|

▦ Have ready cut 6 x 6 grids from 2cm squared paper or invite the children to cut them out. These should be stuck down onto a sheet of paper and the children can write in 0-5 around the grid as shown below.

✗	0	1	2	3	4	5
0	0	0	0	0	0	0
1	0	1	2	3	4	5
2	0	2	4	6	8	10
3	0	3	6	9	12	15
4	0	4	8	12	16	20
5	0	5	10	15	20	25

They can then fill in the products and note the matching halves to the table, along the diagonal.

👤 Give the children a 5 x 5 grid and ask them to write in the numbers one to 25 along the rows. They should then mark or colour differently the multiples of two, three, four and five. The results should look like this:

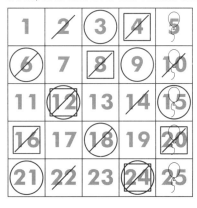

2
3
4
5

2

3

4

5

Closing the lesson

Give the children spot challenges like – 'Which is bigger – the product of two threes or two fours?' etc. and 'Which give the same product – three fours, six twos and two fives?'

Assessment

Child performance	Teacher action
Knows some multiplication facts	Give the children practical opportunities to explore multiplication and give multiplication exercises before returning to a check on all facts up to 5 x 5
Can work to 5 x 5 but still has to compute some multiplications	Give speed tests and mental tests on working out multiplications until the children are very familiar with them
Knows all multiplications to 5 x 5	The learning targets for this theme have been met

Homework

Invite the children to take home Copymaster 60 so that they can play the Bingo game there. Ask the children to make a little book of puzzles about multiplications up to 5 x 5, suitable for younger children. These can be added to classroom or school resources.

Introducing division

Learning targets

On completion of this theme the children should be able to:

1 ➤➤ share out objects and talk about the number of sharers and the size of share

2 ➤➤ record divisions and use the division sign

3 ➤➤ solve simple division puzzles

Before you start

Subject knowledge

Children are commonly introduced to division after the other operations of addition, subtraction and multiplication. However, sharing in everyday life should have featured in their early experience, when the family are eating a meal, or toys are passed out at play group. There are four important features of division that the children should come to know. They are:

- division is repeated subtraction
- division is about the size of share (if four cakes are shared between two people, how many each?)
- division is about how many shares (if four cakes are put into shares of two, how many people can have a share?)
- division is the inverse of multiplication (5 x 5 = 25, 25 ÷ 5 = 5).

Previous knowledge required

Subtraction, multiplication.

Resources needed for Lesson 1

Twenty small toys or other objects for sharing; pictures of marbles such as those shown right, mounted on card, which can be photocopied and cut out (make up so that each group has a set of thirty marble cards); for each pair of children a set of 20 marble cards is also required; Copymaster 62.

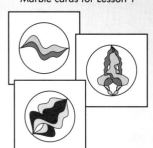

Marble cards for Lesson 1

Chart for Lesson 2

shared by
shared between
divided by
÷

Missing number 'divisions' for Lesson 3

10 ÷ 2 =	6 ÷ 3 =	12 ÷ 4 =	15 ÷ 5 =
2 ÷ 2 =	8 ÷ 4 =	4 ÷ 2 =	20 ÷ 4 =
10 ☐ 5 =	9 ÷ 3 =	3 ☐ 3 =	5 ☐ 5 =
6 ☐ 2 =	8 ☐ 2 =	14 ☐ 2 =	16 ☐ 4 =
18 ÷ ☐ = 6	20 ÷ ☐ = 10	20 ÷ ☐ = 4	18 ÷ ☐ = 9
☐ ÷ 3 = 4	☐ ÷ 3 = 5	☐ ÷ 2 = 8	☐ ÷ 2 = 6

Resources needed for Lesson 2

Chart (see above right); number lines to 50 made up from Copymaster 94; Copymaster 63.

Resources needed for Lesson 3

Missing number division puzzles (see above).

Teaching the lessons

Lesson 1 ①

Key questions

If I share these how many are there each?

If these are put into shares of … how many shares are there?

Vocabulary

Share out, divide, share.

Introduction ⏱10min

 Ask two or three children to stand in front of the class and share some toys or other objects among them. Announce the starting number and say how many sharers, and then ask the children, 'How many each?' Do this several times with different numbers of objects. Then alter the number of children and repeat the sharing again. Do not use any numbers that give remainders as these should be taught once the concept of division is fully mastered (see Theme 22: Remainders).

Then sort a number of toys into piles or 'shares'. For example if twelve toys are set in piles of four, ask the children how many shares of four there are (three). Do several of these calculations.

Activities ⏱35min

 Give each group a set of thirty marble cards (see Resources). Under your direction the children should take a given number of marble cards from the pile and share them out between a suggested number of people in their group, for example share ten marbles between two to find how many each has; or take six marbles, give out shares of two and ask how many people have a share.

Allow each pair of children to have 20 marble cards and a set of problem cards made up from **Copymaster 62**. The children can take turns to set out the arrays of marble cards that make up the shares. Walk around and check that every child has a turn using every card.

Closing the lesson [10min]

Remind the children of work they may have done on fractions by taking a circle of coloured paper and folding and cutting it into two equal pieces and then four equal pieces. Ask the children to pretend this is a cake and talk about sharing and the size of shares. If the children have not met fractions in their mathematics, rehearse again the sharing activity done in the introduction, this time allowing a child to act as 'teacher'.

Assessment

Child performance	Teacher action
Cannot share out objects and talk about the number of sharers and the size of share	Give more practical experience of sharing
Understands sharing but not confident	Allow the children to repeat some of the activities in this lesson
Can share out objects and talk about the number of sharers and the size of share	Move on to the next lesson

Lesson 2 ②

Key questions

What is ... divided by ...?

Vocabulary

Divide, division, sign, repeated subtraction.

Introduction [10min]

Show the children the class chart. Discuss the information. Write a 'sharing' calculation, such as six shared between three, on the board. Underneath write $6 \div 3 = 2$.

Activities [35min]

Give everyone a number line to twenty. Point out that if we divide twenty by two, we can show this as jumps of two along the line from twenty to zero. Allow the children to make these jumps and ask them how many jumps they made. Write $20 \div 2 = 10$ on the board. Try some more divisions under twenty, using repeated subtraction. Point out to the children that division is like taking away or subtracting again and again.

Ask the children to complete **Copymaster 63**.

Closing the lesson [5min]

Give the children ten divisions orally which they must record as you speak. This gives more practice in writing the sign and setting down calculations.

Assessment

Child performance	Teacher action
Cannot record divisions or use the division sign	Give the children more practical sharing work of the kind found in Lesson 1
Records divisions but makes errors	Ask the children to write down divisions given orally
Can record divisions and use the sign	Move on to the next lesson

Lesson 3 ③

Key questions

Can you use the numbers in this division to make a multiplication?

Vocabulary

Division, multiplication, link.

Introduction [10min]

Write some missing number division puzzles using small numbers on the board. Work through a number of examples such as $10 \div 2 = \square$; $9 \div 3 = \square$; $\square \div 4 = 4$ showing them how to solve the puzzles.

Activities [35min]

Ask the children to individually try completing the missing number divisions written on the board (see Resources).

Then write a division on the board such as: $8 \div 4 = 2$. Then write $4 \times 2 = 8$. Ask the children what kinds of calculation they are, and what the links are between them. Try more examples to confirm the link.

Closing the lesson [5min]

Call out multiplications and invite the children to convert them to divisions. Give everyone in the class a turn at answering.

Assessment

Child performance	Teacher action
Cannot solve simple division puzzles	Invite the children to do some practical sharing, and repeat Lesson 1 and 2 activities before re-introducing the division sign and then working on puzzles again
Solves division puzzles with some difficulty	Revise the work done in Lesson 2 before tackling puzzles again
Can solve simple division puzzles	The learning targets for this theme have been met

Homework

Ask the children to list all the times things were shared out in their house in a week. What sorts of things are shared? Are the shares made by counting, cutting, or in other ways?

THEME 21

Dividing by 2, 5 and 10

Learning targets

On completion of this theme the children should be able to:

1 ➤➤ divide by two with confidence
2 ➤➤ do division by five
3 ➤➤ divide by two, five and ten

Before you start

Subject knowledge

Alongside the times tables the children should be able to master a similar set of facts about division. This theme gives them the chance to do just that.

Previous knowledge required

Multiplication, what division is and the use of the sign.

Resources needed for Lesson 1

A chart with the two times table written out on it, Copymaster 64.

Resources needed for Lesson 2

Number lines to 50 made up from Copymaster 94, Copymaster 65, card clock face.

Resources needed for Lesson 3

Copymasters 66 and 67.

Teaching the lessons

Lesson 1 ①

Key questions

Divide this number by two.
What is the outcome of ... divided by two?

Vocabulary

Divide, divided, division, answer, outcome.

Introduction 10 min

▦ Remind the children of their two times table by showing them the chart. Remind them also of the link between multiplication and division. Point out that if they know that three times two is six, they also know that six divided by two is three. Try more examples of this in the two times table.

Activities 35 min

👤 Ask the children to complete **Copymaster 64**.

▦ Point out to the children that dividing by two is halving. Give quick-fire challenges, asking 'What is half of...?'

 Ask each group to compile a set of ten calculations involving dividing by two. Remind the children that the missing number can be in any of these places in the calculation: $6 \div 2 = ?$; $? \div 2 = 3$; $? = 6 \div 2$; $3 = ? \div 2$.

Closing the lesson 10 min

 Swop around each group's missing number divisions and see which group can finish theirs first.

Assessment

Child performance	Teacher action
Divides by two with difficulty	The children may benefit from a work programme that involves multiplication only, until they are confident. Then sharing by two can begin their re-introduction to division
Can divide by two, but has not memorised division facts	Give more practice in solving division by two problems
Divides by two with ease	Move on to the next lesson

Lesson 2 ②

Key questions

Can you divide this number by five?

Vocabulary

Divide, divided, division, answer, outcome.

Introduction 10 min

▦ Ask the children to count aloud the pattern of fives, from nought to sixty. Then allow groups of children to count in turn. Then ask the children to 'countdown' from sixty. Again allow groups and individuals to repeat this counting pattern.

Activities 35 min

▦ Give out number lines to 50 made up from

Copymaster 94. Remind the children that division is repeated subtraction. Demonstrate that if we stand, for example, on fifteen on the number line, we can jump back in fives to nought (subtracting fives). We make three jumps 15 ÷ 5 = 3. Give the children some more examples to try.

 Ask the children to solve the divisions on **Copymaster 65** using their number line.

Ask the children to write out the five times table and alongside it the 'matching' divisions by five, starting thus:

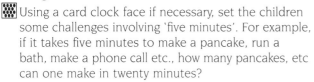

$$0 \times 5 = 0 \qquad 0 \div 5 = 0$$
$$1 \times 5 = 5 \qquad 5 \div 5 = 1$$

Closing the lesson
⬛ 10 min

Using a card clock face if necessary, set the children some challenges involving 'five minutes'. For example, if it takes five minutes to make a pancake, run a bath, make a phone call etc., how many pancakes, etc can one make in twenty minutes?

Assessment

Child performance	Teacher action
Cannot do division by five	Check that the children know the pattern of counting in fives and the five times table. Then practice sharing into fives and among five shares before tackling division again
Can divide by five but lacks confidence	Give the children more practice in activities like those in this lesson
Quickly and accurately divides by five	Move on to the next lesson

Lesson 3 ③

Key questions

Divide this number by two, by five and by ten

What is the outcome of this division?

Which of these numbers can be divided by 2, 5 and 10 – 20, 30, 14, 10?

Vocabulary

Divide, divided, division, answer, outcome.

Introduction
10 min

Ask individual children to call out the pattern of counting in tens. Put some numbers on the board, for example: 30, 20, 40. Ask the children to divide these by ten. With their help find out whether they can be divided by two and five also.

Activities
35 min

Ask the children to work out which products appear in more than one of the 2, 5 and 10 times tables (that is up to 10 x). Their results should be: in two and five – 10 and 20; in five and ten – 10, 20, 30, 40, 50 and 60; in two and ten – 10 and 20.

If the children look carefully they will see that if the counting patterns of two and five are extended beyond the tables, the products of the ten pattern appear in both five and two patterns. This should make the division outcomes easier to work out.

Ask the children to complete **Copymaster 66**.

Allow the children to play the board game that appears on **Copymaster 67**.

Closing the lesson
10 min

Sing number rhymes like 'Ten Green Bottles' changing the words so that repeated subtraction appears in the songs. For example: 'One hundred green bottles... if ten green bottles should accidentally fall'; 'One hundred green speckled frogs...'; 'Ten fat sausages sizzling in a pan, one went pop and one went bang'.

Assessment

Child performance	Teacher action
Cannot divide by two, five and ten	Give the children plenty of sharing practice before embarking on this theme again. Practice of times tables would help with division facts
Divides but needs more practice	Give the children the chance to work on some of the activities presented in this theme again
Can divide by two, five and ten	The learning targets for this theme have been met

Homework

Give the children copies of the game on Copymaster 67 to take home to play.

Ask the children to try doing division on a calculator. For example, they can find out how many two minutes, five minutes and ten minutes slots there are in one hour.

Remainders

Learning targets

On completion of this theme the children should be able to:

1 ➤➤ say what a remainder is

2 ➤➤ find remainders in divisions

3 ➤➤ show they know about approximation and rounding

Before you start

Subject knowledge

Having mastered the concept of division the children need to know how we cope when a number cannot be exactly divided by another. Remainders are going to be important when the children are working with decimals at Key Stage 2. Important strategies for the able mathematician include approximation and rounding, and these are introduced in the context of division in Lesson 3. They also feature in Theme 27: Calculation strategies.

Previous knowledge required

Division.

Resources needed for Lesson 1

Twenty items suitable for sharing (these could be play dough cakes, old greeting cards, felt-tipped pens or other classroom equipment suitable for doing practical division), mathematical apparatus such as Multilink®, Unifix® or similar counting blocks.

Resources needed for Lesson 2

A collection of about fifty small toys or other classroom equipment suitable for doing practical division.

Resources needed for Lesson 3

Five snack packs of biscuits of different kinds or makes (for example, cookies or cheese biscuits) all placed in opaque bags and labelled one to five; Copymaster 68.

Teaching the lessons

Lesson 1 ①

Key questions

Can you say what is 'left over' after this division is done? What is the name for the 'leftovers'?

Vocabulary

Remainder.

Introduction `10min`

Using the sharing items (play dough cakes, old greeting cards, felt-tipped pens or other classroom equipment), and some children to share the things among, remind the children that if we share, say twelve items between four, they will have three each. If there are thirteen items, there will be one left over.

Discuss with the children what happens in their family when there is sharing to be done and it does not work out equally.

Activities `30min`

Give each pair of children some mathematical apparatus, like Multilink®, Unifix® or similar counting blocks. Call out a challenge like 'Share ten between three' and see if they can lay out the appropriate array, showing the remainder.

Invite the children to set out counters or other apparatus to show the solutions to problems set out as shown below.

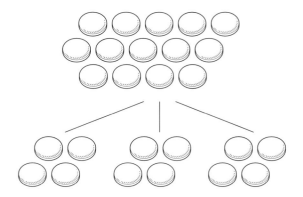

$$14 \div 3$$

remainder

Closing the lesson `15min`

Give each group several cards with numerals on them, calling them remainder cards. Call out a division and ask each group to work it out and show a card indicating the remainder.

Assessment

Child performance	Teacher action
Cannot say what a remainder is	Give the children practical activities involving sharing where there are no remainders. Then look with them at what happens if the total for sharing is increased by one. They should then be able to point to this and call it a remainder
Knows what a remainder is but cannot set it out	Help the children set out some practical divisions where remainders occur
Can set out remainders	Move on to the next lesson

Lesson 2 ②

Key questions

Can you divide this by this?

Is there a remainder here? What is the remainder?

Vocabulary

Remainder.

Introduction ⌷⌷min⌷

▓ Write up some divisions using small numbers (where there will be remainders) on the board and point to them randomly, asking the children to announce the remainder. Write in the answers so that the children can see how to present them.

Activities ⌷⌷min⌷

▓ So that the children are reminded of the sharing aspect of division, set out before them a collection of about fifty small toys or other classroom equipment suitable for doing practical division. Try out some divisions where there are remainders. Begin by setting the total to be shared and ask: 'How many each?' and 'What is the remainder?' Then do some where the total is set and the size of share is decided upon – then ask 'How many shares – and what is the remainder?'

▣ Write some examples on the board such as 14 ÷ 3 = □ remainder □; 13 ÷ 4 = □ remainder □, where the children can do the divisions and write in the remainders.

Closing the lesson ⌷⌷min⌷

▓ Offer the children some outcomes of divisions with remainders to which they have to give the original number. For example, if you say 'three shares of three remainder two', the children should respond with '11'. Here are some examples to try: 'two shares of five, remainder three'; 'three shares of four, remainder two'; 'four shares of three, remainder two'; 'six shares of ten remainder eight'.

Assessment

Child performance	Teacher action
Cannot find remainders in divisions	Teach the children how to do division by sharing real objects. After several short sessions without using remainders, introduce the idea, again using real objects
Finds remainders with difficulty	Give the children more practice at the kinds of activities included in Lessons 1 and 2
Can find and record remainders	Move on to the next lesson

Lesson 3 ③

Key questions

What is your approximation?

Are you going to round up or down?

Vocabulary

Approximate, round.

Introduction ⌷⌷min⌷

▓ Tell the children that they are going to be learning about approximation and rounding, in this lesson. Approximation is used a good deal in real life. Ask the children for some answers to these questions: Approximately how long does it take to get to school? Approximately how many bowls of cornflakes do you get from a pack? Approximately how many biscuits are there in a snack pack? Approximately how much washing powder or liquid does mum or dad need for a full load?

Point out that when we are sharing things out we can often tell approximately how many there will be each. Allow the children to pass around the five snack packs of biscuits and try to feel approximately how many there are in each bag. They can then be asked, for example, if Bag 1 was shared between two children, approximately how many would they have each?

Try out several sharing problems orally, using the bags. Record some of the children's suggestions as shown below.

Bag 1

If shared between 2, approximately how many each

Clare	7
Sean	10
Sophia	5

Activities $\boxed{35\,min}$

 Allow each group to have one bag of biscuits. They can open the bag, lay out the biscuits and then compare the actual contents with the approximations on the board. The biscuits can then be eaten. (Check first that no child has a food allergy or cannot for medical, cultural or religious reasons eat them.)

Invite the children to approximate the numbers and sizes of share on **Copymaster 68**.

Tell the whole class that rounding means saying what a number is approximately, making it easier to use in calculations. We find counting and working with tens easy and might want to round numbers to the nearest ten. Show the children on the board that with numbers ending in one to four units we usually round down. When the number has five units or more it is usually rounded up. Thus 13 can be rounded down to ten, while 26 can be rounded up to 30.

Closing the lesson $\boxed{10\,min}$

Give individual children approximation or rounding puzzles, involving sharing. These are tricky and so you may wish to simply work through more examples on the board.

Assessment

Child performance	Teacher action
Cannot show they know about approximation and rounding	Check that the child can confidently compute using all four operations, before beginning to tackle these strategies again
Beginning to use approximation and rounding	Move on to another theme, checking that the child has more problem solving experience in Key Stage 1
Copes with approximation and rounding with ease	Move on to another theme, checking that the child has more problem solving experience in Key Stage 1

Homework

Reminding children of rounding up or down to the nearest ten, ask them to find out some approximations at home, for example time spent by individuals getting to work or school, in the bathroom or watching TV each day; how many apples the family eats each week or boxes of cereal each month; or how many shirts are washed each week.

Investigations

- Investigate patterns in multiplication tables.
- Find different multiplications that give the same product. For example, the following all have a product of 12:
1 x 12	12 x 1	2 x 6
6 x 2	4 x 3	3 x 4
2 x 2 x 3	3 x 2 x 2	2 x 3 x 2
- Make and investigate multiplication squares, remembering that squares made up of odd numbers are often easier to solve. Make a picture code to depict the numbers in the answer square. Then draw a part-filled square and ask classmates to solve it. Opposite is one such square (based on an ancient 'magic' square, where all the digits 1 to 9 appeared only once).
- Roll two dice and multiply the numbers that the dice show together.

- Use a blank track to invent a game involving multiplying or dividing.
- Draw number lines and make coloured patterns of jumps in 2s, 5s and 10s.

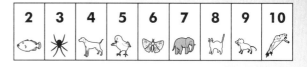

On this square, each row across, down, and diagonally, adds up to 18. Fill in the missing animals.

Assessment

- Check the times table facts the child knows.
- Ask the child to sort things into equal groups and compute a total by repeated addition.

- Group counters in a range of ways, including, for example 1 set of 4; 2 sets of 2; 4 sets of 1.
- Share objects in equal groups.
- Find how many sets of, say, 5 there are in a pile of counters, 1p coins or Centicubes®.

MENTAL ARITHMETIC AND NUMBER PATTERNS

Mental arithmetic is important. It is invaluable to us all to be able to recall the common number bonds in addition, subtraction, multiplication and division in our everyday lives. However, it should be pointed out that there is a difference between memorising facts and learning them by rote. We not only remember better what we understand but we are also able to apply the ideas and facts we understand to new situations.

We cannot expect children to acquire strategies for doing mental arithmetic simply by making them do mental arithmetic! Mental strategies do need to be taught to children. Some children will develop a range of personal methods, whether or not they have this help, but some will not. Thus we need to draw attention to the different ways in which things might be done. For example, here are two ways in which we may do a multiplication: when multiplying 15 x 13, we might think of the product of 15 10s, then the product of 3 15s and add these together; or we might compute 10 13s then calculate half of that (5 x 13) and total the result.

Time needs to be given to getting children to explain their thinking and to share ideas with each other. If formal algorithms are presented to the children as the only ways of doing computations, and imposed on them, this will reduce their mental arithmetic capability. We want children to be able to say, for example, the answer to 'two more than 99' without having to write it down at all, using either horizontal or vertical presentation.

Contrary to popular belief, the widespread use of calculators and , for example, computers at supermarket checkouts that keep running totals, has not diminished the importance of mental arithmetic. It is just as important nowadays to know the 'order' of the amount spent, whether we have enough in our purse, and to approximate and estimate during everyday life.

Looking for patterns

Learning targets

On completion of this theme the children should be able to:

1 ➤➤ find number patterns around them and make such patterns

2 ➤➤ describe odd and even numbers

3 ➤➤ look for and continue patterns in numbers

Before you start

Subject knowledge

This is the part of the mathematics curriculum where children can begin to investigate what used to be called algebra. Pattern is at the nub of mathematics and an understanding of how to search for patterns will make children more confident in their work with numbers and they will enjoy mathematics more.

Note that pattern in a mathematical sense does involve 'repeat'. In art work we often refer to pattern making when talking about line, colour and other aspects of any abstract work. The children will need to be encouraged to make their pattern search and pattern making mathematical – printing shapes or banging a drum is not necessarily making a pattern.

Previous knowledge required

Counting, reading and writing numbers to at least ten for Lesson 1, at least twenty for Lessons 2 and 3. The counting pattern of twos.

Resources needed for Lesson 1

Extra adult help in walking the children around the school; Polaroid® camera and film, if available; art materials, including poster paint made up thick enough for printing, old food trays like that in which meat is sold, synthetic sponge, hard sheet plastic, rollers, paper; scissors; a collection of musical instruments which the children can try (these can include things like tambourines, sticks, chime bars and home made shakers); Lego®, Lasy®, Multilink® or other construction apparatus.

Resources needed for Lesson 2

A row of cut-out card houses with large front doors, as shown below; Copymaster 69.

Resources needed for Lesson 3

Calculators; Copymaster 70; pictures and artefacts from a range of cultures, including patterns where counting has been involved, for example North American Indian, Greek.

Teaching the lessons

Lesson 1   ①

Key questions

Can you find a pattern here?

Count the pattern, how does it go?

Tell us the pattern you are using.

Vocabulary

Number pattern, repeat.

Introduction   15 min

▦ With extra adult help take the children around the built environment of the school. Allow the children to look for patterns and talk about the numbers involved in these. Note down the patterns they see. Some likely locations for detecting number patterns are fencing and railings; brick walls; paving slabs, pavement; roofing tiles; window panes.

If a polaroid camera is available, take photographs of the patterns the children spot.

Activities   30 min

Set up a workshop where there are the following group activities, and the groups can take turns at each activity.

⚫⚫ Print patterns can be made from a paint soaked sponge pad using junk packaging, corks and the like pressed into it, or the paint can be rolled onto a plastic sheet and then the children can make a pattern in the paint before laying a piece of paper over it to print it off. Examples of such patterns are shown below.

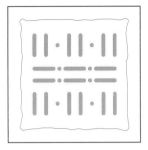 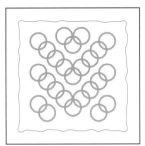

Ask the children to try making patterns using the collection of musical instruments. For example, one loud tap followed by three quieter ones is a pattern that can be repeated.

Using Lego®, Lasy®, Multilink® or other construction apparatus the children can make patterns of colours that repeat in their models

Closing the lesson [5min]

Choose some of the patterns the children have made to hold up to show the class. The child who made the pattern can name the numbers involved. All the children's work can be put on display.

Assessment

Child performance	Teacher action
Cannot find number patterns around them	Giving individual help, show the children some patterns in the world around them, doing the counting again and again. Then allow them several sessions at replicating the patterns they have found
Cannot create number patterns	Give the children plenty of practice at activities like those described in this lesson
Can find and create number patterns	Move on to the next lesson

Lesson 2 ②

Key questions

Is this number odd or even? How do you know?

Vocabulary

Odd, even.

Introduction [10min]

Explain to the children that mathematicians give names to special kinds of numbers, and that they are going to learn to name two kinds in this lesson. Write the numbers 1 to 10 on the board with spaces in

between. Announce that one is an odd number and write 'odd' underneath it. Then explain that every alternate number after one is odd. Write 'odd' under all the other odd numbers displayed. Wipe this work off the board.

Activities [30min]

Ask the children to complete the first part of **Copymaster 69**.

Set up the row of 10 cut-out card houses with large front doors so that all the children can see them. Point out that these are houses on one side of the street and that the first number is two. Write '2' on a small piece of paper and attach it to the first front door with Blu-tack® (on the far left, from the children's point of view). Point out that in this street the odd numbers are on the other side of the road. On this side are the numbers that are not odd. These are called 'even' numbers.

Label the front doors and allow the children to call out what the next even number is each time.

When all the numbers are on the doors ask the children if there is something they know about all these numbers. Some children may note that even numbers are in the counting pattern of twos.

Ask the children to finish the work on the Copymaster 69.

Set up the houses again and ask children to attach the odd numbers to the doors this time.

Closing the lesson [10min]

Ask the children what their house numbers are. Show them that they can look at the last number (numeral, digit or units) and then say whether it is an odd or even number. (Note that numbers ending in zero are even because they are in the counting pattern of twos). Write down all the house numbers in the class and put aside for a homework exercise (see Homework).

Assessment

Child performance	Teacher action
Cannot identify odd and even numbers	Play counting games, where the children, for example, clap 'one', sing 'two', clap 'three', sing 'four' and so on, or say one in a 'squeaky' voice and two in a 'ghost-like' voice and so on. After each count explain that the claps or squeaks are odd, the singing or ghosts are even
Cannot describe odd and even numbers	Revise the counting pattern of twos to help in describing even numbers
Can identify and describe odd and even numbers	Move on to the next lesson

65

Lesson 3

Key questions

Can you continue the pattern?

What comes next?

Vocabulary

Continue, repeat.

Introduction | 10 min |

Write some number patterns in sequence on the board and invite individual children to continue them while the others look on. Here are some examples:

| 2 3 | 2 3 | 2 ... |
| 5 10 15 | 5 10 15 | 5 ... |

Then more complex:

2 7 5 6   2 7 5 ...

Activities | 30 min |

Using the calculator invite the children in pairs to each have a turn at doing this activity.

- Key in '2 + 2 ='.
- Read off the answer.
- Now press '='.
- Look at what happens to the display.
- Keep pressing '=' and find out what happens.

Now try this with other small numbers, predicting how the number pattern will continue.

Invite the children to continue the patterns on **Copymaster 70**.

Arrange a display around the room of pictures and artefacts from a range of cultures, including patterns where counting has been involved. Direct the children's attention to some of the patterns visible. Allow each group to spend time looking at particular items, and then pass them on.

Closing the lesson | 10 min |

Discuss some of the patterns the children have seen in evidence in the pictures and artefacts passed around.

Assessment

Child performance	Teacher action
Cannot seek out patterns in numbers	Give the children plenty of opportunities to note patterns both in their immediate environment and in all parts of the curriculum
Cannot continue patterns in numbers	Allow the children to invent repeat patterns in art, dance, music etc. and talk about these before trying to detect and continue those made by others
Can seek out and continue number patterns	The learning targets for this theme have been met

Homework

Give the children a list of the house numbers of all the children in the class. Invite them to draw two house outlines and on one write the set of odd numbers and on the other write the set of even numbers.

Invite the children to look at fabrics and draw and colour in felt tipped pen some of the patterns they see. This could form part of a stimulating display.

Add, subtract, double and halve to 20

Learning targets

On completion of this theme the children should be able to:

1 ➡➤ show they know by heart additions and subtractions to ten

2 ➡➤ show they know by heart additions and subtractions to twenty

3 ➡➤ double and halve numbers

Before you start

Subject knowledge

It is reported that children in the UK lack some of the mental arithmetic skills that children in some other nations display, and therefore do not achieve highly in mathematics. Certainly, it is a characteristic of numerate people, that they can sometimes 'work things out' without writing them down, and that they may use a variety of methods, some of which they 'invent' for themselves. To give children the opportunity to acquire the capacity to think mathematically, we must give chances in school. This theme is starting this process. Addition is focused on in Lessons 1 and 2. Lessons with similar activities can be devised for subtraction.

Previous knowledge required

Concepts of addition and subtraction, counting patterns of two, five and ten times tables for Lesson 3.

Resources needed for Lesson 1

Large sheets of card or paper and felt-tipped pens (write up patterns of computation), Copymaster 71.

Resources needed for Lesson 2

Sets of pair cards (enough for each pair of children to have a set) made up of the twenty-two numerals shown below mounted on card and cut out.

1	2	3	4
5	6	7	8
9	10	11	12
13	14	15	16
17	18	19	20
0	10		

Resources needed for Lesson 3

Card strips (make number/half number on them), Copymaster 72.

Teaching the lessons

Lesson 1 ➀

Key questions

One and ? make ten? Two and ? make ten?

Tell me four ways of making five.

Vocabulary

Add, plus, addition, sum, number bond, numbers nought to ten, equals.

Introduction ⏱ 10min

▨ Pin up ten large sheets of paper around the room. Explain to the children that they are going to be looking at patterns in addition to ten in this lesson. Stand by the first sheet of paper and write '1' at the top. Then write as follows:

$$0 + 1 = 1$$
$$1 + 0 = 1$$

Ask the children whether there are other ways of making one. Move on to the second large piece of paper and write '2' at the head of it. Now ask for ways of making two. Write up the children's suggestions in order thus:

$$0 + 2 = 2$$
$$1 + 1 = 2$$
$$2 + 0 = 2$$

Continue on the next sheet to make three, and so on, until there are five or six sheets left to complete (matching the number of workgroups in the class).

Activities ⏱ 30min

⚉ Give each group a felt-tipped pen and ask them to complete the pattern of number bonds to make the number assigned to their large sheet of paper (continuing patterns started in the introduction).

▨ Review the work of all the groups, and compare the addition patterns for each of the numbers from one to ten.

▣ Take down the number pattern charts. Ask each child to complete **Copymaster 71** as quickly as they can, giving it to you as soon as they finish. Clip together the children's work labelling the batches, say five or under minutes, six to ten minutes, eleven to fifteen minutes. Stop the children at fifteen minutes and note which children failed to complete the task.

Closing the lesson `10min`

Offer children mental challenges, individually and in pairs. Divide the class into red and blue teams, and ask them to call out the answers to addition challenges in turn. Give parts of each group a turn; for example, say, 'The next two are for the girls in the blue team. Make eight – two and ? five and ?'; 'The next two are for the six year olds with a cat, in the red team'; 'Here are four for the children with white on their socks…'

Assessment

Child performance	Teacher action
Gives no indication that they know by heart additions and subtractions to ten	Allow the children to work with counting apparatus, toys and other classroom equipment in physically pointing and counting and putting sets together. Then over several sessions revise the recording of addition before attempting to commit number pairs to five to memory
Resorts to using fingers or other aids to do additions	Give the children more rapid-fire practice at number bonds until they are very familiar with them
Has ready correct answers to number bond questions	Move on to the next lesson

Lesson 2 ②

Key questions

Give me five ways of making 16.

What do eight add seven make?

Vocabulary

Add, plus, addition, sum, number bond, numbers nought to twenty, equals.

Introduction `10min`

Work in this lesson follows on from the knowledge the children have used in Lesson 1 in this theme. Work through some number patterns on the board, by adding a small number to successive numbers in turn. Here is the 'add one' pattern:

$1 + 1 = 2$	$11 + 1 = 12$
$2 + 1 = 3$	$12 + 1 = 13$
$3 + 1 = 4$	$13 + 1 = 14$
$4 + 1 = 5$	$14 + 1 = 15$
$5 + 1 = 6$	$15 + 1 = 16$
$6 + 1 = 7$	$16 + 1 = 17$
$7 + 1 = 8$	$17 + 1 = 18$
$8 + 1 = 9$	$18 + 1 = 19$
$9 + 1 = 10$	$19 + 1 = 20$

Point out the patterns evident in the arrays.

Activities `35min`

To practice work on pair bonds making twenty allow each pair of children to have a set of pair cards (see Resources). They can lay them out in matching pairs, making 20 (6 and 14, 11 and 9 etc.). They can shuffle them and turn them over, then take turns at flipping over two to try to make a pair (sum to 20).

Another game is to share out half each, and see who can make most 'twenties' out of pairs of cards in their hand. The children can then work out more games of their own.

Give each child a number card from those used for the games above. Call out a total to make, and if their number does not meet or exceed this total they should move around the room and find the child holding their 'pair' number. Thus the child holding '7', should, when 14 is called out, look for another child holding a '7' card. (Note that some number cards may not have been assigned to anyone).

Closing the lesson `5min`

Allow the class to chant in sequence the number pairs to twenty thus, nineteen add one, eighteen add two, seventeen add three etc.

Assessment

Child performance	Teacher action
Cannot show they know by heart additions (and subtractions) to twenty	Revise the children's work on number bonds to ten, using practical apparatus and recording before trying to commit the bonds to memory. Then work again to twenty
Knows some of these number bonds	Give more practice at oral work and game playing using number pairs to twenty
Readily answers these number bond challenges	Move on to the next lesson

Lesson 3 ③

Key questions

What is half of …?

What is double …?

The number … is double what?

The number … is half of what?

Vocabulary

Double, half, halved, times two.

Introduction `5min`

Ask the children if they know what 'double' means. Show them that one doubled is two, two doubled is four and so on up to ten. Ask some quick-fire questions needing doubles up to 20 as answers.

Activities

👤 Ask the children to do the first part of **Copymaster 72** where they can write in the doubles discussed in the introduction.

▦ Point out that we can do the reverse of doubling and that we call this halving. Give the children some examples like those on the Copymaster.

👥 Give every pair 14 card strips. Invite them to fold them as shown here and write on them a 'double number' and the 'half numbers:

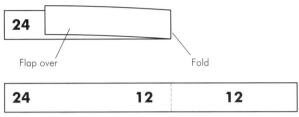

Flap over   Fold

Card strip opened out

▦ Write on the board the counting pattern of fives in a column. Ask the children to call out 'Five – five doubled is ten, ten – ten doubled is twenty' and so on up to sixty.

👤 Ask the children to complete the remainder of Copymaster 72.

Closing the lesson 5 min

▦ The class should call out the pattern of tens and doubles. Then repeat this, counting down from 120, and calling out the half numbers, thus 'One hundred and twenty, one hundred and twenty halved is sixty'.

Assessment

Child performance	Teacher action
Cannot double and halve numbers	Work on the two times table and doubling and halving products there. Then repeat the lesson
Can double and halve numbers but these are not memorised yet.	Give more quick-fire practice at doubling and halving until these numbers are memorised
Answers doubling and halving challenges with ease	The learning targets for this theme have been met

Homework

Invite the children to make a concertina test book of number patterns, like this:

doubles	halves	+ to 10	
1 → 2	1 → 1	0 + 10	1+1 = 2
2 → 4	4 → 2	1 + 9	1+1+1 = 3
3 → 6	6 → 3	2 + 8	1+1+1+1 = 4
4 → 8	8 → 4	3 + 7	1+1+1+1+1 = 5
5 → 10	10 → 5	4 + 6	1+1+1+1+1+1 = 6
6 → 12	12 → 6	5 + 5	
7 → 14	14 → 7	6 + 4	

They can bring the completed book to school where they can be photocopied and swopped around for other children to check and replicate.

Missing numbers, function machines and number trails

Learning targets

On completion of this theme the children should be able to:

1 ➤➤ find missing numbers in calculations
2 ➤➤ solve and devise function machine calculations
3 ➤➤ solve and devise number trails

Before you start

Subject knowledge

This theme offers opportunities for children to demonstrate how adept they are in mental calculation. The underlying strategy has to do with looking at the information one has, the 'clues' to what the outcome should be, and then using this information to deduce what is 'missing'.

Previous knowledge required

All four operations.

Resources needed for Lesson 1

Copymaster 73 (game).

Resources needed for Lesson 2

A box such as a shoe box for each group, paper pieces on which numbers and functions can be written, Copymaster 74.

Resources needed for Lesson 3

Large sheets of paper for each pair of children, felt tipped pens, sheets of card.

Teaching the lessons

Lesson 1 ①

Key questions

What is the missing number here?

Vocabulary

Compute, computation

Introduction 15min

▦ As the children will have done additions, subtractions, multiplications and divisions before attempting this theme they should have developed some personal strategies for working out, in their heads, some ways of finding what's missing in a calculation. Just in case they do not have these skills it is worth explaining all the steps in finding a missing number.

Write up on the board, a calculation such as 5 + ? = 9. Some children will say 'it is four' straight away. Invite them to explain how they did it. They may say they counted in their heads from five up to the total of nine to get the missing four; or they took the five away from the nine to find the missing four; or they 'just knew' it was four. Work the problem out on the board, using all the ways the children suggest.

Try doing the same activity with subtraction, multiplication and division problems.

Activities 30min

👤 Give the children some missing number problems like those shown below, to try out. They may have rough paper to work on, but should try to see if they can work them out in their heads. If they make notes these can be handed in so that the teacher can see the methods they are trying.

Add	Subtract
$6 + \square = 9$	$11 - \square = 6$
$14 + \square = 17$	$18 - \square = 15$
$\square + 16 = 19$	$\square - 25 = 25$
$\square + 50 = 56$	$\square - 19 = 20$
$6 + \square + 9 = 32$	$\square - 15 = 31$

Multiply	Divide
$2 \times \square = 4$	$6 \div \square = 3$
$10 \times \square = 100$	$20 \div \square = 4$
$\square \times 5 = 10$	$\square \div 10 = 5$
$\square \times 4 = 12$	$\square \div 2 = 12$
$2 \times \square \times 2 = 8$	$12 \div 4 = 9 \div \square$

👥 Ask the children to play the missing number game on **Copymaster 73**.

Closing the lesson 5min

▦ Call out some quick-fire missing number calculations and see if the children can answer them.

Assessment

Child performance	Teacher action
Cannot find missing numbers in calculations	Revise all four operations, gradually introducing missing numbers into different positions in the calculations
Can find missing numbers in some calculations	Inspect the children's work to discover where the child is lacking in skill or confidence. Work through these kinds of calculation before asking the children to complete more missing number challenges
Finds missing numbers with ease	Move on to the next lesson

Lesson 2 ②

Key questions

What is the output here?

What is the input here?

What is this function machine doing?

Vocabulary

Function machine, operation, input, output.

Introduction [10 min]

Place a large box on a table in front of the class. Tell the children that this is going to be a function machine. Write, for example, '+2' on a piece of paper; show the children and place this inside the box. Tell the children that this is an 'add two' machine. Write a number on another piece of paper (for example '7') and push it through a slot in the side of the box. Ask the children what will happen to this number inside an 'add two' machine. Write the numeral '9' on another piece of paper and feed this out of the box on the other side as shown here:

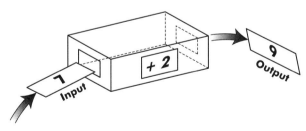

Try with more numbers keeping the function the same. Then change the function to , for example, '−5' and pass more numbers (exceeding five) through the box, showing what happens to them.

Activities [35 min]

Allow the children to make and operate their own function machines. They can all take turns at being the teacher. Remind them to try adding, subtracting, multiplying and dividing.

Ask each child to try to complete **Copymaster 74** where there are several function machines operating.

Closing the lesson [5 min]

Using the function machine box show the children how some more complex functions like '×2, +4' and '−1, ÷2' will work.

Assessment

Child performance	Teacher action
Cannot solve function machine calculations	Give the children plenty of simple computation practice. Then take some computations and treat them as function machine problems, showing which part of the calculation would happen 'inside the machine'. Then repeat this lesson
Beginning to solve and devise function machine calculations	Give the children more practice in doing the activities set out in this lesson
Can work with function machines	Move on to the next lesson

Lesson 3 ③

Key questions

What comes next in this number trail?

See if you can work back from the number that comes at the end of the trail.

What number is missing here?

Vocabulary

Number trail.

Introduction [15 min]

Draw a simple number trail on the board such as the one shown below.

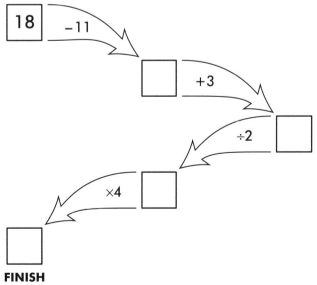

With the children's help, fill in the missing numbers.

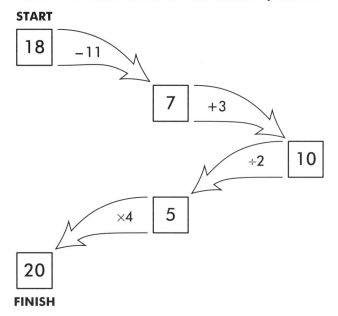

START

18 −11

7 +3

÷2 10

×4 5

20

FINISH

Alter the starter number in the trail and show what happens to all the other outcomes along the trail.

Activities
⏱ 35min

 Give each pair of children rough paper, a large sheet of paper and felt-tipped pens. Invite them to draw a rough design for a number trail and then transfer it to the large sheet, making it as neat as possible. Mount each trail on a sheet of card and pin it up on the wall.

 Allow everyone to go around the room and try out as many of the trails as they can.

Closing the lesson
⏱ 10min

Ask some of the pairs of children to give the solutions to their trails, and answer questions the children have.

Assessment

Child performance	Teacher action
Cannot solve or devise number trails	Give the children the chance to practise computation and missing number problems, before returning to this lesson again
Solves and devises number trails but finds them difficult	Allow the children the time to solve all the number trails devised in this lesson. Then give them several opportunities to devise a trail, in different sessions
Can work on number trails with ease	Move on to another theme

Homework

Invite the children to look in puzzle books and comics and magazines to find more number challenges and trails. A common form of puzzle is shown below.

Answers

	1	5		4	
8		0		6	
5	1	4	6	2	
7		2		7	
9	4	3	0		
	7			3	
	9	1	5	0	
5	3	2		5	
	9	8	6	2	

	5		
	0		
	4		
	2		
	3		

Put in these numbers

15
128
532
3052
4627
9862
8579
9150
9430
47939
51462

72

Money problems

Learning targets
On completion of this theme the children should be able to:

1 ➤➤ recognise and write prices using decimal notation

2 ➤➤ work out the cost of a shopping list

3 ➤➤ work out change when shopping

Before you start

Subject knowledge
Shopping and using money is an arena in which we most frequently apply our mathematical knowledge. In order to shop with confidence we need to develop mental strategies to estimate, approximate and compute the sums involved. This is, therefore, a very important area of mathematics for the children to experience. Note that the children have not worked with decimals in other contexts at Key Stage 1, so the concept of the decimal point has not been raised here. It is important that the children should be able to interpret prices correctly and know which part is pounds and which part is pence.

Previous knowledge required
Vocabulary of shopping, coins and equivalence.

Resources needed for Lesson 1
A purse with plastic replica coins in it, five toys or food packs, price labels for the objects with the price written in words on one side and in decimal notation on the other, a set of coins including 1p, 2p, 5p, 10p, 20p, 50p, £1, calculators, Copymaster 75.

Resources needed for Lesson 2
A collection of shopping receipts, a class 'shop' with empty food packs which can be priced for sale, price cards, Copymaster 76.

Resources needed for Lesson 3
Real coins or replica plastic coins, Copymasters 77 and 78.

Teaching the lessons

Lesson 1 ①

Key questions
Read me the price of this.

What does £4.56 mean?

Vocabulary
Price, cost, pound, pence, decimal.

Introduction 15 min
Talk to the children about their experiences of going shopping. Invite a child to stand at the front as a shopkeeper holding a food pack. Another child can be given a purse containing plastic replica coins. Point out to the children that this is only a game to show what happens when we shop. Allow the child shopping to give some money to the shopkeeper and take the goods. Describe what is happening.

Write '10p' on the board and ask the children what the 'p' means. Then write up some other prices such as twenty seven pence, 82 pence, £4.39.

Discuss what these say and the various ways they

can be written. Note that it is incorrect to mix '£' and 'p' in expressing prices. Thus £2.48 is correct or 248 pence is correct but £2.48 pence or £2.48p is incorrect.

Activities 30 min
Set five toys or food packs up in front of the children, and place on each a price card with the price written out in words. Here are examples:

Four pounds and thirty-three pence	Six pounds and ninety-nine pence	Twenty pounds fifty	Fourteen pounds forty	Nine pounds ninety-nine
£4.33	£6.99	£20.50	£14.40	£9.99

(on reverse of cards)

Talk about the prices, and turn each over to show how the price is written in figures.

Ask the children to work through **Copymaster 75**.

Give a calculator to each pair of children and invite them to try out the challenges they did on Copymaster 75, taking turns at doing one each. Give help to the children who cannot bring the digits they wish onto the screen.

Closing the lesson   `10 min`

▦ Give the children a test, asking them to write down the value of each of our coins (1p, 2p, 5p, 10p, 20p, 50p, £1). Then ask them to write some other sums of money which include pounds and pence.

Assessment

Child performance	Teacher action
Cannot recognise and write prices using decimal notation	Help the children to look at the prices of things in a class 'shop' and talk again about their experience of shopping. Work through some example prices in words and numbers. Repeat this lesson
Has some difficulty sometimes in using decimal notation	Give the children more practice in recording money sums using decimal notation
Copes successfully with decimal prices	Move on to the next lesson

Lesson 2   ②

Key questions

How much does this cost?

How much do all these items cost?

What is the total spent on this shopping?

What sum of money do we need for this shopping?

Vocabulary

Cost, price, sum, total.

Introduction   `10 min`

▦ Share with the children some of the items, prices and totals on the collection of shopping receipts.

Activities   `30 min`

❖ Allow each group a chance to exchange money for 'goods' in the class shop. They can do this by turns while the other activities are in progress.

👥 Using two supermarket receipts with many items on them, the children can take turns to key in the costs of the items on a receipt on the calculator and see whether they reach the same total as on the receipt itself.

👤 Ask the children to complete **Copymaster 76**.

Closing the lesson   `10 min`

▦ Lay out an array of toys or packs from the class 'shop' with prices prominently attached. Invite a child to come to the front and announce which three items they will buy. Ask the class to call out how much these will cost in total.

Assessment

Child performance	Teacher action
Cannot work out the cost of a shopping list	Invite the children to practice play buying things in a little play shop. Make the items cost only pence, and begin by summing two, then three, then four items. Then gradually increase the prices so that the child starts to spend over £1. Then repeat Lessons 1 and 2 in this theme
Finds the task of working out shopping totals difficult	Give more practice in activities similar to those set out in this lesson
Can sum the costs of shopping	Move on to the next lesson

Lesson 3   ③

Key questions

How much will you get in change?

What is the change here?

Vocabulary

Change.

Introduction   `10 min`

▦ Using real coins, talk about what happens when you shop for something costing, for example, 3p, 14p, 26p, 58p and so on and have not got 'the right money'. Allow the children to contribute by telling you what coins to use and what the change might be.

Activities   `30 min`

👤 Ask the children to complete **Copymaster 77**

▦ Explain to the children that shopkeepers often give us our change while 'counting on' from the sum we have spent. Ask two children to stand at the front. Call one the shopkeeper and the other the customer. Ask the children to pretend that the customer has spent 77p in the shop. He or she gives the shopkeeper a pound coin. The shopkeeper then passes coins back to the customer like this 'Seventy-seven – seventy-eight, seventy-nine, eighty' (gives three one penny coins), 'ninety' (gives one ten pence coin), 'one pound' (gives one ten pence coin). Practice more examples like this with other pairs of children.

👥 Allow the children to play the shopping game on **Copymaster 78**. They play in pairs or two teams. Each team has £3 to spend. This can be made up using plastic replica coins, or the children will need to record what they spend, and the coins they would need. At each throw of the dice the player moves that number of squares. They cannot go through a shop and beyond in one go, but must wait for their next throw.

Closing the lesson

🪟 Call out a sum that a customer has spent, how much is given to the shopkeeper and ask the children to call out what is the change. If they are hesitant, lay out on the desk the sum given in coins and the change necessary in coins.

|10 min|

Assessment

Child performance	Teacher action
Cannot work out change when shopping	Give the children more chances to practise shopping in class, with you, yourself as the shopkeeper, so that the change expected can be discussed in each transaction

Can work out change but lacks confidence	Give the children more chance to do activities like those set out in this lesson
Confident when shopping and in calculating change	The learning targets for this theme have been met

Homework

Invite the children to collect supermarket receipts at home, and play at keying in the individual items on a calculator and checking totals.

Calculation strategies

Learning targets

On completion of this theme the children should be able to:

1 ➡➡ decide on how best to order numbers in a calculation

2 ➡➡ use partitioning and multiples of ten as aids to computation

3 ➡➡ know how to check their work

Before you start

Subject knowledge

Children are using calculation strategies when engaged on all the activities within this book. In this theme some of these strategies are spelled out for the children so that they can enlarge their own repertoires.

Previous knowledge required

All four operations, tens and units.

Resources needed for Lesson 1

Dice (enough for two for each pair of children), Copymaster 79.

Resources needed for Lesson 2

Mathematical apparatus for setting out tens and units.

Resources needed for Lesson 3

Completed work from other sessions (for example calculations in their exercise books done from the board or completed Copymasters 34, 39 and 64).

Teaching the lessons

Lesson 1 ①

Key questions

Which number will you take first?

What is the best order to do this calculation? Why do you say that?

Vocabulary

Order, calculation, larger, smaller.

Introduction | 10 min |

▦ Ask the children to try 3 + 7. Ask them how they did it. Some children may say 'I started with the seven and added on (or counted on) the three.' Point out to the children that, when we are adding, the numbers can be taken in any order. It makes sense to start with the higher number and count on from there because there is less work to do.

Write up some more additions on the board and ask the children which is the number to start with. Work through them explaining what you are doing. Here are some example additions:

2 + 17 = ?	4 + 8 + 1 = ?
3 + 14 = ?	2 + 26 = ?
5 + 44 = ?	3 + 5 + 51 = ?
6 + 72 = ?	2 + 7 + 90 = ?

Rub out the answers to these additions once they are all complete.

Activities | 35 min |

👤 Ask the children to try for themselves the additions you have just worked through at the start of the lesson.

👥 The children should take turns to throw two dice of different colours (having named one dice the 'tens' dice and the other the 'units' dice). They then write down the numbers they have thrown. Thus, if player one throws a two on the tens dice and a six on the units dice '26 +' is written down. Then if the other player throws '53', the calculation is written 26 + 53 = . The children can draw an arrow pointing down above the number they intend to start with and then they can work out the calculation. (In this case they should start with 53). The children should have time to do at least ten additions like this.

👤 Invite the children to complete **Copymaster 79**.

Closing the lesson | 10 min |

▦ Invite the children to 'add 10' to numbers. Call out 6, 11, 34, 56 etc. and allow them to call back the answers. Then ask them to 'add 11' by adding ten and then one more. Then ask them to 'add five' to some numbers. Finally ask them to 'add six' by adding five and then one more.

Assessment

Child performance	Teacher action
Cannot determine an order for approaching an addition	Allow the children to become adept at adding small numbers together,

before tackling a larger number added to a small number. Help them in many short sessions, using counting apparatus as well as mental skills. When appropriate repeat the activities set out in this lesson

| Knows that it is a good idea to take the larger number first but makes mistakes | Give the children more practice at the activities set out in this lesson |

| Is quick and accurate, and starts with the bigger number in additions | Move on to the next lesson |

Lesson 2 ②

Key questions

Can we write this calculation another way that makes it less tricky to do?

Can you use what you know about the pattern of tens here?

Vocabulary

Strategy, calculation.

Introduction `10min`

Point out to the children that adding seven and twelve gives the same answer as adding seventeen and two, thus $7 + 12 = 17 + 2$. Ask the children whether they find it easier to add seven and twelve or seventeen and two. They probably find the latter easier because they can count on two quickly. Try some more example such as $8 + 22 = ?$, $6 + 42 = ?$, $8 + 53 = ?$, $9 + 72 = ?$

Activities `35min`

Allow the children to have some mathematical apparatus to help them in completing another set of examples like those in the introduction to the lesson.

Remind the children that their knowledge of the counting pattern of tens can be very helpful in doing calculations. Write on the board $39 + 7 =$. Point out that 39 is only one less than 40, 40 add 7 would be 47, so the answer here is one less – that is 46. Try out $48 - 21$. Here 21 is only one more than twenty. $48 - 20 = 28$, so the answer to $48 - 21$ is going to be one more than that – that is 29.

Give the children a chance to do more calculations such as $29 + 8$, $52 - 31$, $67 - 29$, $8 + 77$, $17 + 38$, $62 - 19$, $41 - 11$, $48 + 7$, $39 + 9$, $99 - 16$, $59 - 18$, $76 - 67$. Walk around and ask them about the methods they are using.

Closing the lesson `5min`

Invite the children to round numbers you call out to the nearest ten such as 18, 29, 37, 48, 51, 62, 77, 88.

Assessment

Child performance	Teacher action
Cannot use partitioning and multiples of ten as aids to computation	Give the children more practice in looking for number patterns, counting in fives and tens, breaking numbers into their constituents and simple mental arithmetic. Then revisit Lessons 1 and 2 in this theme
Understands how to use calculation strategies but lacks confidence	Give the children more chance to talk about how they are doing calculations and to practice rounding and partitioning
Can use these strategies to good effect	Move on to the next lesson

Lesson 3 ③

Key questions

What can you do to check this?

How do you know this is correct?

Vocabulary

Check, calculation, correct, error.

Introduction `15min`

Ask the children what they do to check whether they have done calculations correctly. Talk to the children about some of the ways people use such as $34 + 46 = 80$, check by doing $80 - 46$ or $80 - 34$; $4 \times 3 = 12$, check by trying 3×4 or $12 \div 3$ or $12 \div 4$. Look carefully at the answer. In addition and multiplication the answer is bigger than the starting numbers. In subtraction and division the answer is smaller than the starting numbers.

Activities `30min`

Allow the children to look together at some of the work they have done in other sessions. This will all have been marked, but the children can still work out ways in which the calculations could be checked. Completed calculations in their exercise books done from the board or completed Copymasters would serve as good starting points. The children will also need rough paper to work on.

Ask the children to record the answers and how they can be checked, to do more calculations such as $15 + 8$, $92 - 33$, $17 - 11$, $29 + 18$, $6 + 6 + 13$, $19 - 8 - 7$, $76 - 11 - 5$, $50 + 5 + 20$.

Closing the lesson `5min`

Write up a completed calculation such as $25 + 14 = 40$ on the board and ask the children if it is correct. They should say it is not correct. Ask which children added or subtracted to check their own answer. Here are some suggestions for methods they may have used: they could have checked by adding $14 + 25$, $20 + 10$ and then $5 + 4$; or by rounding the 14 to 15 and saying 25 + 15 = 40 so the answer here is only 39; or they could have checked by subtracting 40 – 14, or 40 – 25.

Assessment

Child performance	Teacher action
Does not know how to check work	Take the children through a method at a time, in different sessions, and starting with small numbers and addition. Then when they are confident allow the children to look at calculations involving larger numbers and other operations
Can check some calculations	Give the children plenty of opportunity to check their own work and that of others and talk about what they are doing
Checks calculations using a range of methods	The learning targets for this theme have been met

Homework

Give the children a set of calculations to try out. They can record how they did them, and how they checked them. They can also try out the calculations and all the ways of checking on a calculator.

Investigations

- Play games that involve mental arithmetic. All simple 'chance' board games can be played with two dice and the numbers on both added, or the larger subtracted from the smaller before a move is made.
- Look for patterns in addition and multiplication squares. For example, there are patterns to be seen here:

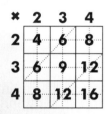

Dotted lines mark some patterns

- Investigate the patterns in times tables.

- Look for patterns on number lines.
- Make computation patterns in circles. Here is a pattern made when we add 2 and look at the last digit each time:

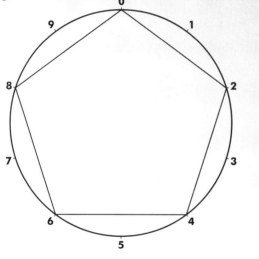

Assessment

- Give rapid-fire short tests, lasting only a couple of minutes.
- Ask the children to discuss the methods they use.

Write these on the board and allow the other children to comment and share.
- Ask the children to devise tests that could be given to classmates.

NUMBER DATA

Handling data about numbers can be seen as 'applied' mathematics in much the same way that work on measures is applied. Data handling and the pictorial representation of data is the most ubiquitous form of mathematics nowadays. We cannot pick up a newspaper, watch the TV news or listen to the radio for long without seeing or hearing the results of a survey. People are commonly suspicious of statistics, but if we do not make sure we allow children to gain a mastery of everyday data, they will almost certainly be duped by a misrepresentation or false analysis at some time.

When working with young children we often use block graphs (see opposite) as one of the common starting points. They are an example of a way of presenting data which is relevant to children at all ages and stages of their lives. Many number patterns can be explored through pictorial representation.

Handling data brings together all aspects of the mathematics curriculum. To handle and understand data appropriately we need to have an appreciation of shape, space and measures, and not merely number. As soon as children start organising their counts they are handling data, and thus data work is not divorced from what they themselves see as part of understanding mathematics.

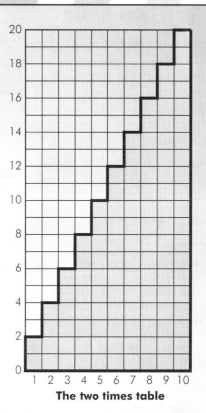
The two times table

The children can also employ Ideas to do with matching, mapping and sets which they have met in other mathematics lessons. An understanding of these concepts is fundamental to the ability to make data pictures and interpret them. It is, for example, important that we distinguish between continuous and discrete data. We cannot produce line graphs using discrete data, though this misuse and misrepresentation of data is often seen in the press!

Number pictures

Learning targets

On completion of this theme the children should be able to:

1 ➤➤ sort objects out according to criteria and make a record of sorts
2 ➤➤ do mapping exercises and make a record of these
3 ➤➤ create and interpret pictograms where a picture represents one object

Before you start

Subject knowledge

Here is an opportunity for children to apply their number knowledge and have experience in the logical decisions involved when we sort out, the mapping considerations when we match things, and how counts can be represented as pictures.

Previous knowledge required

Counting, matching.

Resources needed for Lesson 1

Classroom chairs, cushions and a stool; collections of objects that the children can use for sorting including: small toys, card shapes, wooden blocks, objects from the natural world such as sticks, cones and pebbles, classroom equipment such as pencils, crayons, felt-tipped pens; Copymaster 80.

Resources needed for Lesson 2

Each group will need pictures of the following

stuck on card: five faces of children, five dogs, five drinks, five toys, one adult who could be a teacher; large pieces of rough paper and felt-tipped pens (or ribbons or strips of card); catalogues, magazines, scissors and paper glue; Copymaster 81.

Resources needed for Lesson 3

The resources required for Lesson 1; Copymaster 82; cut out paper cake outlines, such as the one shown below, (enough for one for each child) on which the child can write their name.

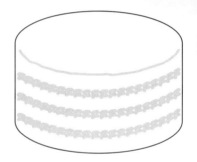

Teaching the lessons

Lesson 1   ①

Key questions

Can you sort these things into different colours?

Put all of these that are the same shape together

Why do you think I have put all these together?

Sort these into different groups and we shall try to work out how you have sorted them.

Vocabulary

Sort, similar, the same, match.

Introduction   10 min

▦ Gather together at least one classroom table, chairs, cushions and the stool. While the children look on say, 'I am going to sort these out. I am going to put all the things I think go together here.' Place the chairs, cushions and stool on one side and ask the children why they think you have put them together. Tell everyone it is because all but the table are for sitting on. Now gather the things together again and

re-sort them according to four legs and no legs (include three legs as a category if the stool has three legs). Again ask the children how they have been sorted this time. Try again with another criterion (hard/soft is one example).

Activities   40 min

⚇ Ask each group to take turns at sorting a collection of objects put before them. Walk around and offer criteria for the sorting sometimes, and sometimes allow the children to use their own criteria. Allow the groups to continue with this activity until every child has had a go.

▦ Draw a collection of pictures on the board and then separate them into sets (by drawing them again) and placing them together. Point out to the children that this is a record of a sort.

👤 Ask the children to complete **Copymaster 80**.

Closing the lesson   5 min

▦ Draw out about six children from the class and sort them out, placing them in groups. Ask the children to give reasons why they are sorted in these ways. Some suggestions for sorting are: girls/boys; blond/ not blond; cardigan or jumper/no cardigan or jumper.

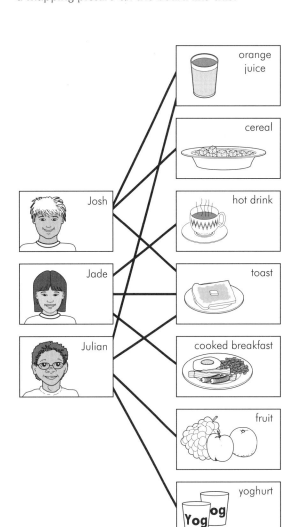

Assessment

Child performance	Teacher action
Cannot sort objects out according to criteria	Give children practical sorting activities, particularly in everyday settings (for example sorting socks from a 'play' wash basket, or getting the red pencils out from a mix of colours)
Sorts but uncertain of criteria and/or cannot make a record of sorts	Give more practice in activities like those in this lesson
Can sort and make a record	Move on to the next lesson

Lesson 2   ②

Key questions

Which should I join up?

Can you match these?

Vocabulary

Mapping, join.

Introduction   〔10 min〕

 While the children look on, hold up each of the five pictures of children and each of the five drinks. Using Blu-tack® stick the child pictures on the board and, some distance away stick on the drinks. Announce that every child wants a drink and join them up as shown below.

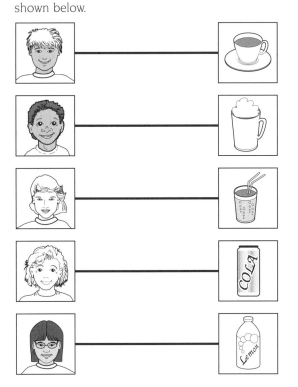

Take the pictures of the children off the board and hold up the adult picture. Stick the teacher picture on the board and say that the teacher needs three drinks. Draw three cups of tea and join them up as shown above right.

Activities   〔35 min〕

 Each group should be given the pictures of the five faces of children, five dogs, five drinks, five toys, and one adult who could be a teacher (see Resources). They can then use large pieces of rough paper and felt tipped pens (or ribbons or strips of card) to make mapping pictures showing, for example, five children for a teacher, five children with a toy each, a child with five toys etc.

Invite the children to complete **Copymaster 81**.

Closing the lesson   〔5 min〕

Ask three children what they eat for breakfast. Create a mapping picture on the board like this:

orange juice

cereal

hot drink

Josh

toast

Jade

cooked breakfast

Julian

fruit

yoghurt

Yog og

Assessment

Child performance	Teacher action
Cannot do mapping exercises	Give more practical work in mapping
Cannot record mapping exercises effectively	Give more practice in recording mappings before repeating activities like those in this lesson
Can do and record mapping	Move on to the next lesson

Lesson 3   ③

Key questions

What shall we put here on the chart?

What does this symbol mean?

Vocabulary

Picture, pictogram other words related to the kinds of data used.

Introduction   15 min

 Tell the children that mathematicians put number information in pictures called charts. Tell them that they can help make a chart. Give every child the cake outline on which they can write their name (see Resources). Allow each child to place their cake where it goes on a big chart that says 'five year olds and six year olds' (or whatever the range of ages is in the class), like this:

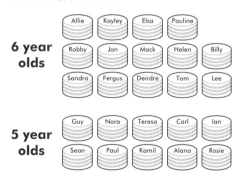

Point out that the chart tells us how many children of different ages in the class. Ask the children what each picture represents (it means one child).

Activities

 In their workgroups the children can sort out how many dogs and cats they have. They can set out a row of counters for cats and a row of counters for dogs. This can be recorded on **Copymaster 82**. Each counter means one pet.

Ask each child to colour a bat to show each child in the picture on Copymaster 82 who is playing a bat and ball game.

Closing the lesson   10 min

Allow a child to throw a floor dice repeatedly. Every time a six is thrown draw a dice on the board. This will be a pictogram of the number of times a six came up in the game.

Assessment

Child performance	Teacher action
Cannot create and interpret pictograms where a picture represents one object	Give the children lots of practice in setting up pictograms that show objects in front of them or class events they are familiar with
Is not yet confident in creating and interpreting pictograms	Give more practice of the kind tried out in this lesson
Can create and interpret pictograms	The learning targets for this theme have been met

Homework

Ask children to create a mapping picture showing what all the people in their family eat for breakfast.

THEME 29 | Charts and graphs

Learning targets

On completion of this theme the children should be able to:

1 ➤➤ draw Venn and/or Carroll diagrams
2 ➤➤ interpret and draw frequency tables
3 ➤➤ interpret and draw block graphs

Before you start

Subject knowledge

In this theme the children are learning some of the formally accepted ways of presenting number information. They will need to be thinking logically in order to extract information, and make a mental picture of outcomes in order to draw charts.

There are several steps in the process of gaining the skill, not only to access information in a chart made by someone else, but also to gather information and compile a chart of one's own. It may be that the pace of these lessons is rather too fast for some of the children in the class. The lessons can be replicated using different kinds of data each time, until the children can readily not only interpret but also make these kinds of pictures.

In Lesson 1 the focus is Carroll diagrams. Again this same lesson pattern can be used in order to give the children experience of Venn diagrams. Venn diagrams appear in *Learning Targets: Key Stage 1: Shape, Space and Measures.*

Previous knowledge required

The idea that number information can be put in a picture

Resources needed for Lesson 1

Numbers from 1 to 20 on card; card shapes including plenty of triangles, quadrilaterals and circles in at least two colours; the pictures on Copymaster 86 could be coloured and stuck on card for this exercise, and there are more pictures on Copymaster 95 for this purpose; Copymasters 83 and 84.

Resources needed for Lesson 2

Day-by-day weather record for two school weeks, school cafeteria menu for several weeks, Copymaster 85.

Resources needed for Lesson 3

Make a corrugated card grid like those found in wine boxes to separate the bottles of wine, a collection of small toys, 2·5cm (1in) squared paper.

Teaching the lessons

Lesson 1 ①

Draw Venn and/or Carroll diagrams

Key questions

Can you put these into two sets?
Can these be sorted again?

Vocabulary

Sort, set, sub-set, diagram, Carroll.

Introduction ⏱10min

▨ Using two canes or metre sticks place them across one another on a classroom desk, as shown right.

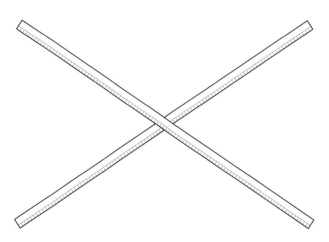

Now look at the numeral cards with the children. Sort them out into odds and evens. Point out that you have made two sets. Now look at each set and say that you are going to sort again according to whether the numbers appear in the pattern of counting in fives. The outcome is four subsets. These can be arranged in the sectors of the 'crossed metre sticks'. Ask the children to describe each subset and then give it a label as shown below.

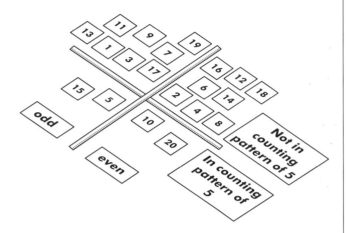

Ask individual children again to identify what is in each subset.

Now repeat the exercise using some or all of the card pictures, and labelling the subsets. Here are some ways of sorting the images found on **Copymaster 86**: plants/not plants; tulip/not tulip; edible/not edible; animal/plant.

Activities [30min]

Ask the children, in their groups, to try some more sorts using first one and then another criterion. They can use **Copymaster 83** as a base board and small pictures and numerals for the sorts.

Ask the children to complete **Copymaster 84**.

Closing the lesson [15min]

With clean hands and a new copy of Copymaster 83 sort a large pack of liquorice allsorts by two criteria (for example liquorice on the outside, or no liquorice/liquorice in the sandwich or the middle and then colours black and white, or not black and white). Once the sorting has been discussed the children may have a liquorice allsort each. This should serve to remind them of what they now know about 'all sorts'.

Assessment

Child performance	Teacher action
Cannot understand and interpret Carroll diagrams	Give the children more practical opportunity in sorting things out before trying practical work on sub sets and Carroll diagrams
Can interpret ready-made Carroll diagrams but finds it difficult to create them	Help the children to create their own Carroll diagrams, which they can record and then talk through
Can interpret and create Carroll diagrams	Move on to the next lesson

Lesson 2 ②

Key questions

What does this chart tell us?

What does this part of the chart show?

How many here?

What else does the chart tell you?

Vocabulary

Chart, frequency.

Introduction [5min]

Ask the children how often they eat a meal each day, how often they wash their hands, walk the dog, read a book, go out to play, and change their clothes. Then ask them how often they do some things each week, for example, read a comic, go shopping with mum or dad. Point out that when we say how often something happens we could say how frequently it happens. We can make number pictures to show how frequently things happen. This is called a frequency chart.

Activities [40min]

Display a day by day weather record that has been kept for two school weeks (this could come from a school archive, but will probably make a bigger impression on the children if they have collected the information). Write the days of the school week on the board and alongside them the weather symbol to show the weather conditions. The chart may look something like the one shown below.

Ask each group to look at the school cafeteria menu and choose an item, which is not served every day, for example, shepherd's pie or cheese flan. They should then see on which days these were served and create a frequency chart. This can be drawn up on a large sheet of paper, with picture symbols for the food item.

Show the children the efforts of all the groups, so that they can comment on outcomes.

Ask the children to interpret the frequency charts they find on **Copymaster 85**.

Closing the lesson `10 min`

▓ Ask four children to stand in front of the others and give each a book from the class library. Tell the children to pretend that the books have been borrowed from the class library, say ten, eight, three and seven times, respectively. Invite a child to begin a frequency diagram, using a book to represent a 'borrowing', on the blackboard. Other children can help complete the drawing while the class look on.

Assessment

Child performance	Teacher action
Cannot interpret and draw frequency tables	Give the children more practice in making mathematical pictures of a range of kinds
Attempts to interpret and draw frequency tables but lacks confidence	Give more examples of frequency charts where a symbol represents a single object or event for the children to inspect, copy and interpret
Can create and interpret frequency tables	Move on to the next lesson

Lesson 3 ③

Key questions

What does this graph tell us?

How can this information be put in a block graph?

Where does this entry go in the graph?

What does this column mean?

Vocabulary

Interpret, block graph.

Introduction `10 min`

▓ Using a corrugated card grid, set out a small collection of toys so that a three dimensional block graph is made like the one here:

Ask individual children to say, for example, how many teddies there are, how many toys altogether and the difference between the number of cars and the number of dolls.

Activities `35 min`

👤 Give each child a sheet of squared paper and invite them to make a picture showing the toy collection arranged in a block graph as in the introduction.

⚫⚫ Give each group a similar collection of coloured blocks in three or four colours. Ask the groups to arrange them in towers of different colours and then colour these towers, alongside one another, to make a block graph on their squared paper.

▓ On the board show the children how the graph of block colours can be drawn using squares. Quiz the children about the final graph, which should look something like the illustration below (depending on the colours of blocks available in class, and how many of them there are).

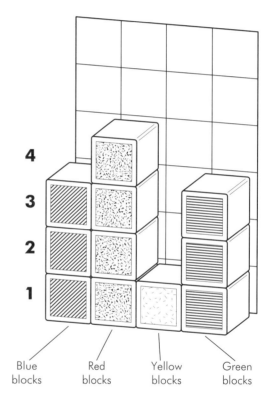

| | Blue blocks | Red blocks | Yellow blocks | Green blocks |

Here are some suggested questions to ask the children: How many blocks are there altogether? What is the difference between the numbers of yellow blocks and green blocks?

Closing the lesson `10 min`

▓ Return to the activity used as the introduction to this lesson, and using different toys, allow a child to set up the 'block graph' and pose the questions about it.

Assessment

Child performance	Teacher action
Cannot interpret and draw block graphs	Ask the child to sort and count small collections of objects, laying them out in matching columns as shown on page 86.

85

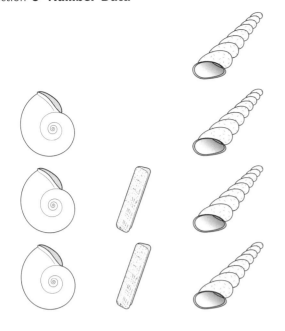

Then help the children transfer this work to a grid on paper. Then try several other examples before making one for themselves

Does not demonstrate confidence when working with block graphs	Give the children more practice, particularly in transferring number data onto a graph and interpreting graphs
Can work with block graphs	The learning targets for this theme have been met

Homework

Ask the children to look carefully at two consecutive old copies of *Radio Times* or other TV listings magazine and record for two or more weeks the frequency of their favourite programmes, for example 'Blue Peter' is commonly on four times a week, and some soap operas feature several times too.

Investigations

- Help the children to find out some information from one another and create information pictures. Examples could include: favourite colours; favourite cartoon characters; number of people that live in their house; birthday months; favourite TV programme.
- Investigate and show number patterns like the 2 and 5 times tables.
- Access information from CD ROMs, picture books, magazines and library books in order to make picture tables and charts.

Assessment

- Set out some information about a topic the children may have been studying in another part of the curriculum. Examples might include projects on dinosaurs, big cats, story books, health. Ask the children to discuss or try out ways of setting out the information.
- Ask the children to make a tally record of events and then question them about what they have done and what the tally tells us.

Colour and count.

Join up to match.

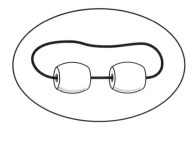
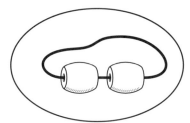
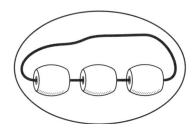
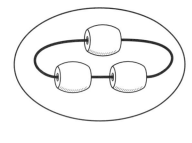
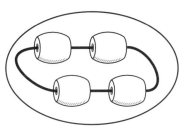
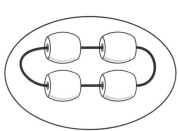

Colour the set with **more**. | Colour the set with **less**.

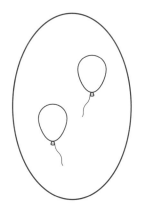 or

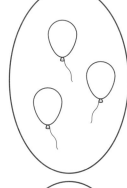 or

Make a mark for each toy.

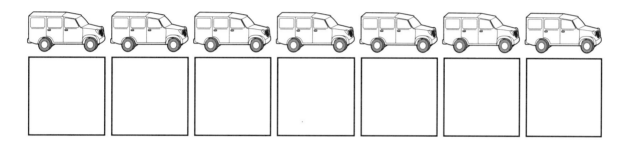

How many?

Write how many.

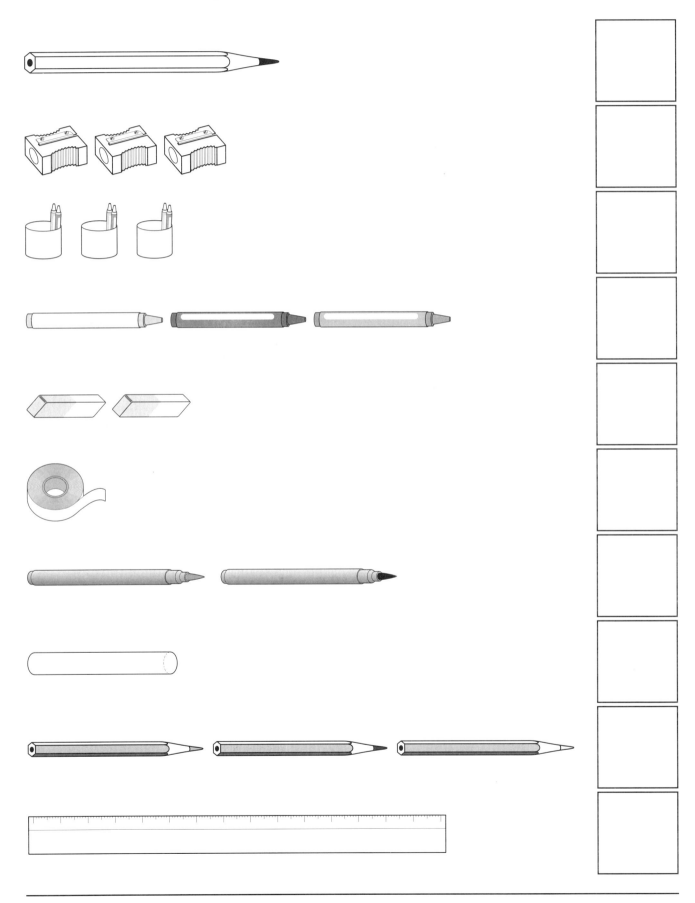

Write in the words and numbers.

six

Copy _____

| 6 | 6 | 6 | 6 | 6 | 6 | 6 |

Copy ___ ___ ___ ___ ___ ___ ___

How many? Write the number. Write the word for the number.

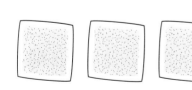 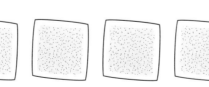 

Count the flags

Draw a line to join each numeral to its set.

1

2

3

4

5

6

7

8

9

10

11

12

13

14

15

16

17

18

19

20

Bingo baseboards

19	12	3
16	8	11

15	5	7
17	2	10

4	18	6
13	1	7

9	20	14
2	10	5

14	18	11
1	9	4

8	3	13
20	15	19

16	1	12
5	10	19

14	6	8
17	3	11

Take turns. Throw the dice. ○ Ring the number you throw if it is on your beetle.

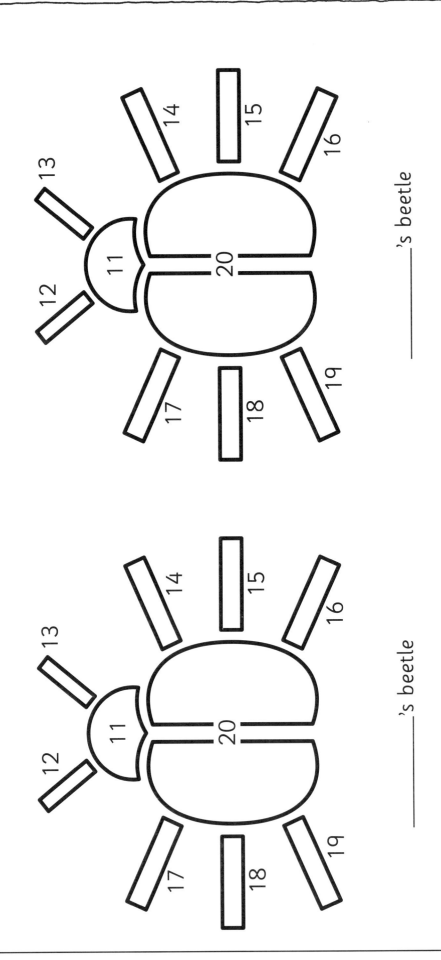

_____'s beetle

_____'s beetle

Count to 20

Write in the numerals to show how many.

Write numbers to 20

Write in the missing numbers and words.

1   2   3   4   5   ☐   ☐   8   9   ☐

11 ☐ ☐ ☐ ☐ ☐ ☐ ☐ ☐ ☐

one   two   three   ☐   ☐

six   ☐   ☐   ☐   ten

☐   ☐   ☐   ☐   ☐

☐   ☐   ☐   ☐   twenty

Write the numbers 1 to 20 on the beads.

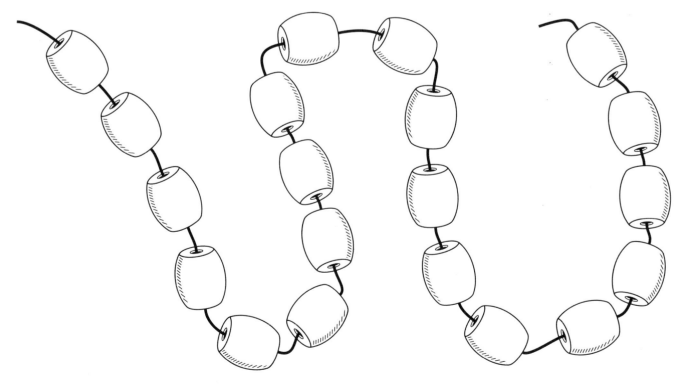

Write small numbers in order

Write in the missing numbers.

First, second and third

Take 3 beads out of the bag. Colour a row of beads. Write:

first	**second**	**third**

_____	_____	_____

_____	_____	_____

_____	_____	_____

_____	_____	_____

Write in each dog's position.

Write here 1st		Write here first

Ordinal number

Tim Sara June Milton Dan Mick

Who is first? _____

Where is Mick? _____

June is second. True? Yes ☐   No ☐ tick

Who is third? _____

Where is Milton? _____

Who is 5th? _____

Who is second? _____

Tim is not 1st. True? Yes ☐   No ☐ tick

Counting in tens to 100

Count in 10s. Write in the numbers.

| 10 | | | | | | | | | 100 |

How many tens?

forty [ ] **ninety** [ ] **ten** [ ]

sixty [ ] **twenty** [ ] **thirty** [ ]

Write the number words.

10	_____	60	_____
20	_____	70	_____
30	_____	80	_____
40	_____	90	_____
50	_____	100	one hundred

Write the numbers.

5 tens [ ]   **7 tens** [ ]

Number words to 100

one	two	three	four	five	six	seven	eight	nine	ten
eleven	twelve	thirteen	fourteen	fifteen	sixteen	seventeen	eighteen	nineteen	twenty
twenty-one	twenty-two	twenty-three	twenty-four	twenty-five	twenty-six	twenty-seven	twenty-eight	twenty-nine	thirty
thirty-one	thirty-two	thirty-three	thirty-four	thirty-five	thirty-six	thirty-seven	thirty-eight	thirty-nine	forty
forty-one	forty-two	forty-three	forty-four	forty-five	forty-six	forty-seven	forty-eight	forty-nine	fifty
fifty-one	fifty-two	fifty-three	fifty-four	fifty-five	fifty-six	fifty-seven	fifty-eight	fifty-nine	sixty
sixty-one	sixty-two	sixty-three	sixty-four	sixty-five	sixty-six	sixty-seven	sixty-eight	sixty-nine	seventy
seventy-one	seventy-two	seventy-three	seventy-four	seventy-five	seventy-six	seventy-seven	seventy-eight	seventy-nine	eighty
eighty-one	eighty-two	eighty-three	eighty-four	eighty-five	eighty-six	eighty-seven	eighty-eight	eighty-nine	ninety
ninety-one	ninety-two	ninety-three	ninety-four	ninety-five	ninety-six	ninety-seven	ninety-eight	ninety-nine	one hundred

Use counting apparatus.

Make these numbers using counting apparatus. Draw in what you used.

tens	units	tens	units	tens	units
2	**6**	**7**	**2**	**1**	**8**

tens	units	tens	units	tens	units
4	**3**	**5**	**9**	**6**	**6**

Large numbers

1 627	91 727	561
3 710	192	5 602
10 714	303 716	755
5 831	17 480	516 729
323	9 119	67 342
520 142	838	8 793
90 183	123 679	126
4 317	88 412	219 568

Hundreds, tens and units

Write how many units.

| 78 | | units | | 511 | | units |

| 902 | | units | | 35 | | units |

How many tens?

| 29 | | tens | | 786 | | tens |

| 591 | | tens | | 19 | | tens |

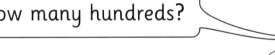

How many hundreds?

| 412 | | hundreds | | 662 | | hundreds |

| 976 | | hundreds | | 266 | | hundreds |

Write these numbers.

four hundred
and sixteen

two hundred
and thirty

ninety-nine

seventy-six

Birds on a wall

Cut out the bird strip. Cut down between each bird to the base strip. Fold all birds back.

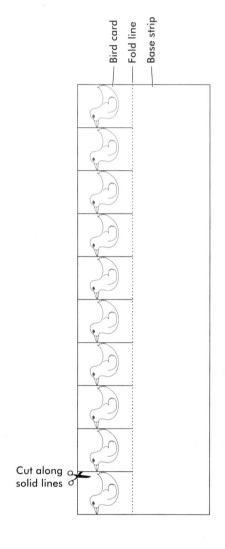

Bird card
Fold line
Base strip

Cut along
solid lines

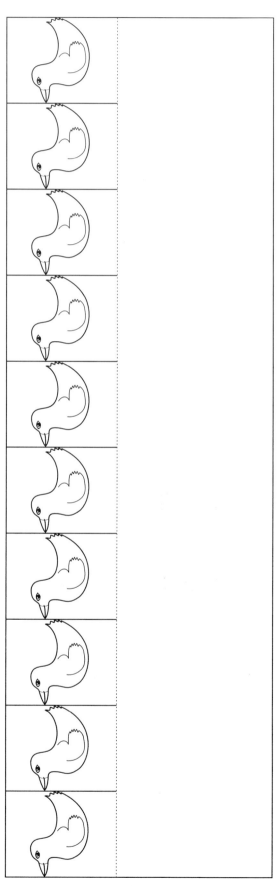

Draw more and count

Draw one more and count.

Draw two more and count.

Draw three more and count.

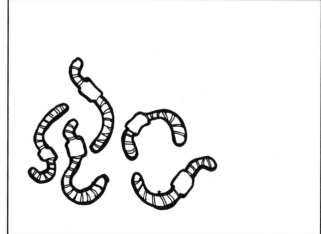

Find the totals

Count how many in each row of sets.

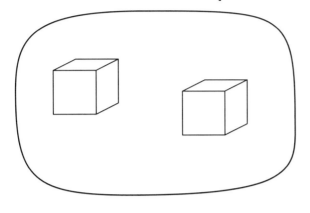
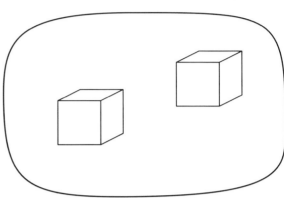

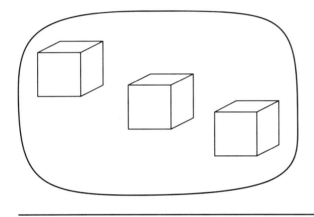
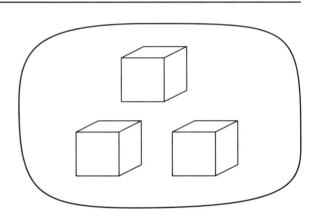

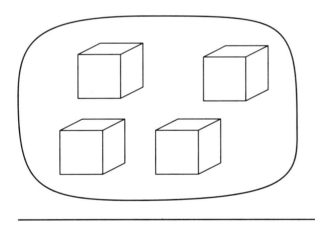
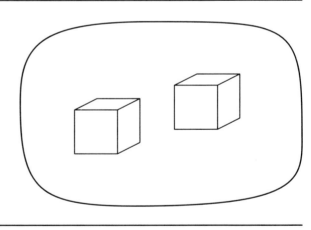

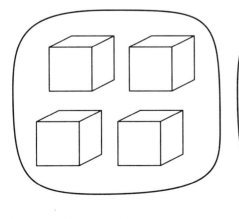
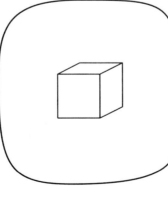
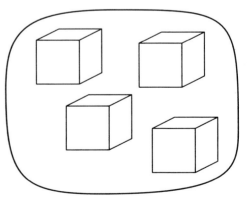

How many altogether?

Draw how many altogether.

 and  make

 and  make

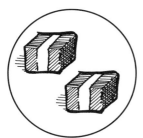 and 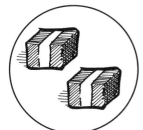 make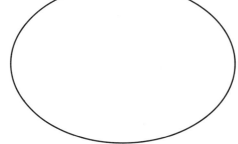

 and  make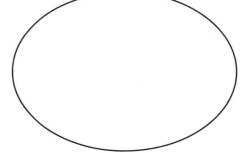

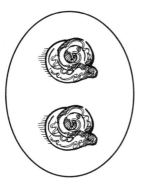 and 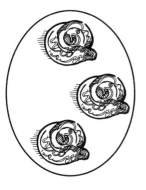 make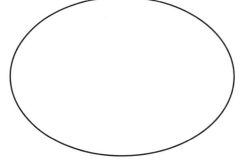

Number bonds to nine

Write in number symbols

☐ + ☐ = ☐ ← Write in the sum

Write in signs

110

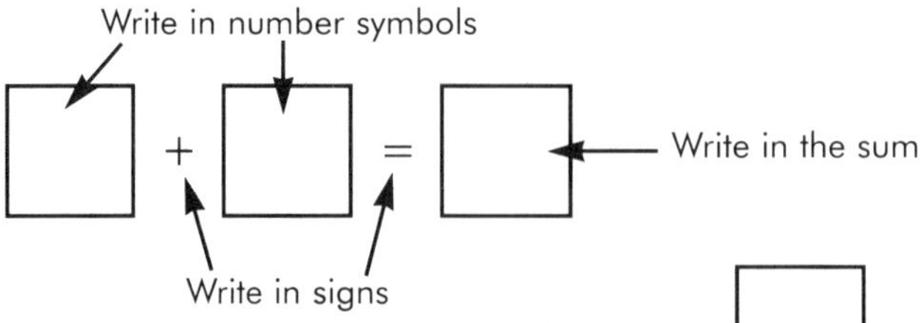

Number trails to ten

Put the numbers on the noses.

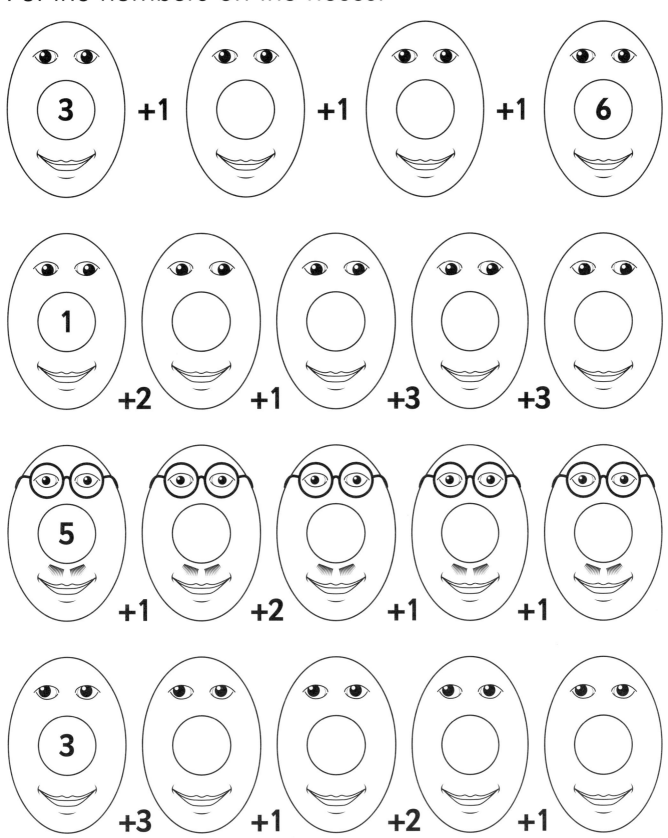

Make some more trails.

Cats on a wall

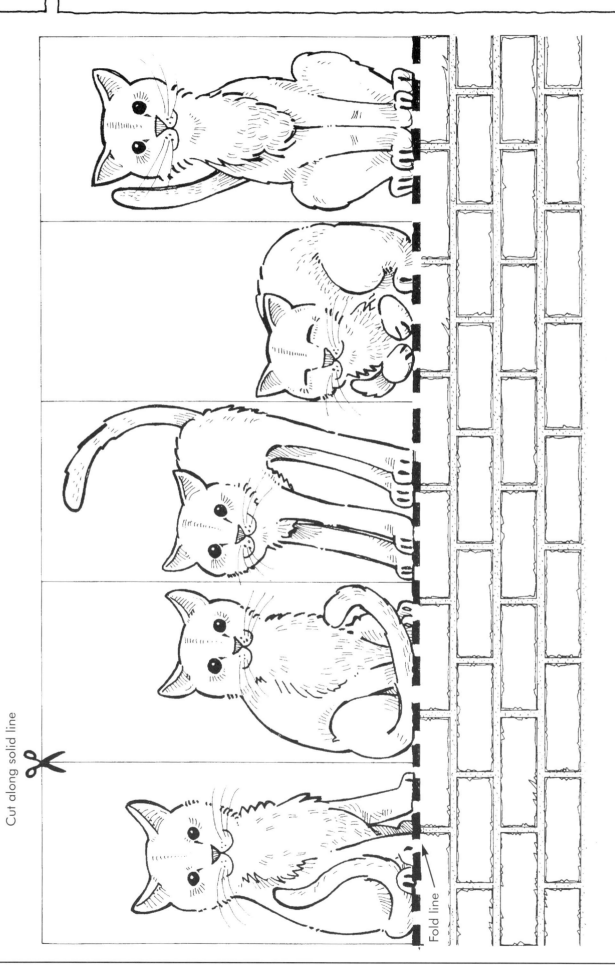

Cut along solid line

Fold line

Draw the pictures. Fill in the numbers.

5 sheep

take away 3

leaves ☐ sheep

☐ dogs

take away ☐

leaves ☐ dog

☐ hens

☐ hens

☐ hens

☐ pigs

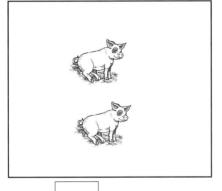

☐ pigs

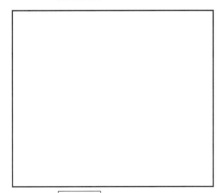

☐ pigs

Adventure playground game

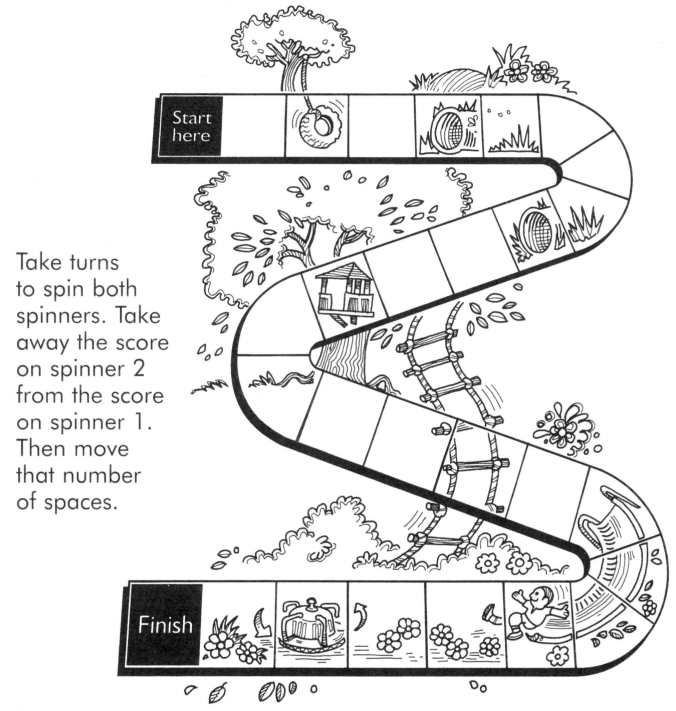

Take turns to spin both spinners. Take away the score on spinner 2 from the score on spinner 1. Then move that number of spaces.

Stick this part of the page onto card. Cut out the spinners and playing pieces. Push a spent match through the centre of each spinner.

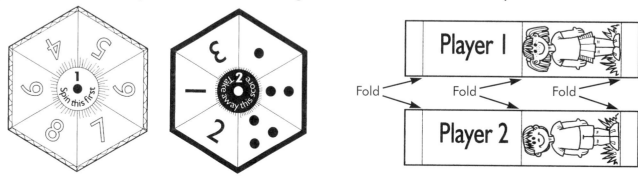

Mapping

Draw in the mapping lines.

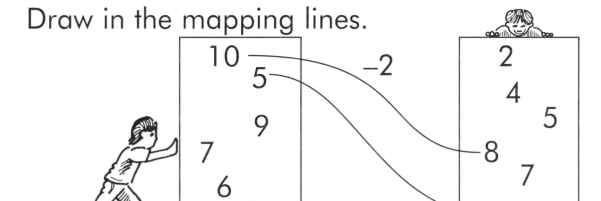

10
5
9
7
6
4

−2

2
4
5
8
7
3

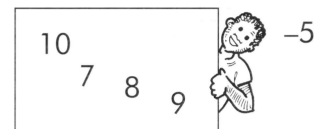

10
7   8   9

−5

2   4
3   5

10
5
9
7
6
4

−3

2
4
1
6
7
3

10
5
6
7
8
9

−1

6
4
5
8
7
9

−4

0
4
5
3
2
1

Subtraction and equals signs

Put in the signs and solve the subtractions.

| 5 | ☐ | 3 | ☐ | 2 | | 4 | ☐ | 1 | ☐ | ☐ |

| 6 | ☐ | 4 | ☐ | ☐ | | 10 | ☐ | 6 | ☐ | ☐ |

| 3 | ☐ | 1 | ☐ | ☐ | | 8 | ☐ | 6 | ☐ | ☐ |

| 9 | ☐ | 7 | ☐ | ☐ | | 10 | ☐ | 9 | ☐ | ☐ |

| 7 | ☐ | 6 | ☐ | ☐ | | 6 | ☐ | 3 | ☐ | ☐ |

| 5 | ☐ | 1 | ☐ | ☐ | | 7 | ☐ | 3 | ☐ | ☐ |

| 8 | ☐ | 5 | ☐ | ☐ | | 9 | ☐ | 5 | ☐ | ☐ |

| 3 | ☐ | 2 | ☐ | ☐ | | 8 | ☐ | 1 | ☐ | ☐ |

| 7 | ☐ | 2 | ☐ | ☐ | | 4 | ☐ | 2 | ☐ | ☐ |

| 8 | ☐ | 3 | ☐ | ☐ | | 3 | ☐ | 3 | ☐ | ☐ |

| 2 | ☐ | 1 | ☐ | ☐ | | 9 | ☐ | 1 | ☐ | ☐ |

Subtraction (missing numbers)

Fill in the missing numbers.

I am good at finding missing numbers, are you?

What's missing here?

$7 - \boxed{} - 2 = 2$ $4 - \boxed{} = 3$

$9 - \boxed{} = 3$ $10 - \boxed{} - 1 = 2$

$8 - \boxed{} - 1 = 2$ $4 - \boxed{} = 2$

$\boxed{} - 6 - 1 = 2$ $\boxed{} - 9 = 1$

$\boxed{} - 5 = 2$ $\boxed{} - 1 - 5 = 3$

$\boxed{} - 8 - 1 = 0$ $\boxed{} - 7 = 2$

$10 - \boxed{} - \boxed{} = 4$ $2 - \boxed{} = 0$

Fill in a subtraction of your own.

$\boxed{} - \boxed{} - \boxed{} - \boxed{} = \boxed{}$

Find the difference

Spot the difference.

Write in the difference between these numbers.

The difference between:

9 and 5   is   ☐

8 and 2   is   ☐

6 and 1   is   ☐

10 and 6   is   ☐

7 and 3   is   ☐

5 and 1   is   ☐

7 and 1   is   ☐

9 and 2   is   ☐

Card 1	Card 2
6 + 11	1 + 15
19 – 13	2 + 17
11 – 9	13 – 13
13 + 5	15 – 9
7 + 11	11 – 8
5 + 12	3 + 11
4 + 7	7 + 6
16 – 8	9 + 10
15 – 10	10 + 10
11 + 3	8 + 12

Card 3	Card 4
7 + 4	2 + 14
17 – 7	5 + 12
20 – 13	16 – 13
10 + 6	18 – 9
12 + 4	10 + 6
15 – 9	6 + 9
17 – 8	4 + 16
19 – 12	8 + 6
11 + 7	17 – 14
9 + 5	11 + 3

Card 5	Card 6
8 + 8	3 + 14
18 – 8	13 + 5
1 + 11	14 – 11
0 + 14	4 + 10
6 + 7	8 + 7
13 – 6	7 + 11
14 – 9	12 – 10
17 – 3	16 – 13
18 + 2	19 – 14
19 – 11	9 + 6

Card 7	Card 8
7 + 8	4 + 12
9 + 9	1 + 16
16 – 7	12 + 8
11 + 7	13 + 2
7 – 5	16 – 15
2 + 8	19 – 17
9 – 0	1 + 15
10 + 9	3 + 16
12 + 7	20 – 11
20 – 19	7 – 2

Card 9	Card 10
4 + 11	1 + 13
10 – 6	5 + 9
5 + 13	11 + 7
15 – 3	6 + 12
3 + 11	13 – 11
11 + 7	17 – 13
16 – 2	2 + 16
2 + 9	7 + 8
8 + 7	9 + 9
9 + 10	8 + 8

$1 + 2 + 4 + 10 = \boxed{}$

$7 + 3 + 6 + 1 = \boxed{}$

$2 + 2 + 2 + 2 + 2 + 2 + 2 + 2 + 2 + 2 = \boxed{}$

$4 + 4 + 4 + 4 = \boxed{}$

$5 + 5 + 5 + 5 = \boxed{}$

$20 - 10 - 10 = \boxed{}$ $18 - 3 - 3 - 3 = \boxed{}$

$14 + 6 = \boxed{}$ $15 + 5 = \boxed{}$

$17 + 3 = \boxed{}$ $8 + 7 = \boxed{}$

$19 + 0 = \boxed{}$ $7 + 8 = \boxed{}$

$11 + 1 = \boxed{}$ $9 + 8 = \boxed{}$

$13 + 2 = \boxed{}$ $19 + 1 = \boxed{}$

$17 - 6 = \boxed{}$ $11 - 5 = \boxed{}$

$19 - 9 = \boxed{}$ $14 - 8 = \boxed{}$

$13 - 7 = \boxed{}$ $17 - 9 = \boxed{}$

$15 - 1 = \boxed{}$ $20 - 0 = \boxed{}$

Linking addition and subtraction

Add and subtract.

5 + 4 =	16 + 2 =
4 + 5 =	2 + 16 =
9 – 5 =	18 – 2 =
9 – 4 =	18 – 16 =
9 + 1 =	3 + 2 =
1 + 9 =	2 + 3 =
10 – 9 =	5 – 2 =
10 – 1 =	5 – 3 =
7 + 8 =	10 + 1 =

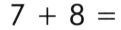

Make sets of four additions and subtractions here.

19 – 9 =	7 + 4 =
16 – 5 =	13 – 12 =

Number bonds to 20

Make ten.

1 +
2 +
3 +
4 +
5 +
6 +
7 +
8 +
9 +
10 +

Make 20.

1 +   11 +
2 +   12 +
3 +   13 +
4 +   14 +
5 +   15 +
6 +   16 +
7 +   17 +
8 +   18 +
9 +   19 +
10 +   20 +

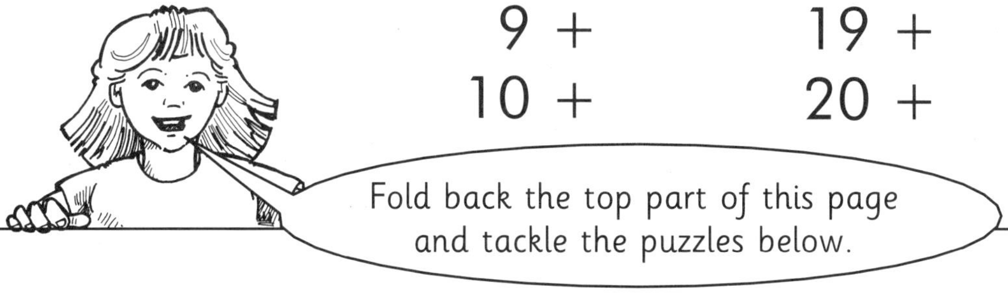

Fold back the top part of this page
and tackle the puzzles below.

7 + 8 =

19 – 10 =

11 + 2 =

16 – 8 =

8 + 8 =

2 + 13 =

$$
\begin{array}{r} 11 \\ +\ \ 4 \\ \hline \end{array}
\qquad
\begin{array}{r} 16 \\ -\ 11 \\ \hline \end{array}
$$

$$
\begin{array}{r} 14 \\ -\ \ 8 \\ \hline \end{array}
\qquad
\begin{array}{r} 17 \\ -\ \ 9 \\ \hline \end{array}
$$

$$
\begin{array}{r} 19 \\ -\ 11 \\ \hline \end{array}
\qquad
\begin{array}{r} 20 \\ -\ 10 \\ \hline \end{array}
\qquad
\begin{array}{r} 9 \\ +\ 3 \\ \hline \end{array}
\qquad
\begin{array}{r} 7 \\ +\ 5 \\ \hline \end{array}
$$

Homework card game

Cut out cards. Mix them up. Match answers to sums.

9 + 7	16	6 + 11	17
8 + 7	15	5 + 7	12
7 + 7	14	4 + 7	11
6 + 7	13	11 + 4	15
9 + 5	14	11 + 3	14
9 + 4	13	13 + 4	17
11 + 7	18	13 + 5	18
11 + 9	20	13 + 6	19
12 + 8	20	13 + 7	20
5 + 11	16	9 + 3	12

Addition of tens and units

Draw in the apparatus you used to help you do these sums.

46 + 33	25 + 54	72 + 17
T | U	T | U	T | U
+	+	+

38 + 61	82 + 15	24 + 62
T | U	T | U	T | U
+	+	+

T U	T U	T U
3 4	2 7	5 2
+ 2 7	+ 5 6	+ 3 9

'T' and 'U'. That's turtles and umbrellas isn't it?

T U	T U	T U	T U
3 3	2 9	4 1	7 6
+ 5 7	+ 1 9	+ 5 3	+ 1 7

T U	T U	T U	T U
1 9	2 2	4 5	2 9
+ 7 2	+ 6 7	+ 3 6	+ 4 4

T U	T U	T U	T U
2 1	4 2	1 8	6 3
+ 7 6	+ 2 9	+ 7 4	+ 3 6

Number stories

Lorry driver Ted is collecting washing machine parts. He has to keep a total of the number of packs as he collects parts from several factories. Add them up as he goes along.

 At Factory 1 he collects 25 packs of controls.

At Factory 2  he collects 37 spinner drum packs,

making a total of packs. At Factory 3  he

picks up 39 casing packs. The total is now packs.

At Factory 4  he completes his job and his

final total is 99 packs. How many packs

came from factory 4?  packs.

Write a number story about a flower grower or a farmer.

Coins – making totals

Write how many pence.

 5p   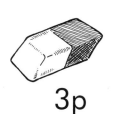 3p    10p   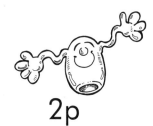 2p    8p

 + = _____ pence

 + = _____ pence

 + = _____ pence

 + = _____ pence

 + = _____ pence

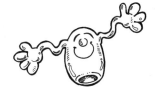 +  = _____ pence

 +  +  = _____ pence

Spend and get change

Go shopping! Draw around coins for the change.

 3p  5p  10p  13p

What you buy	The amount you give the shopkeeper	The change
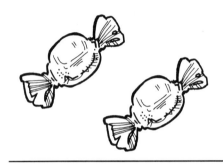		

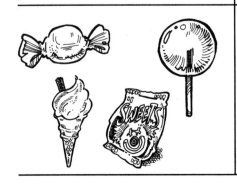		

Play the spend and save game.

What you need:
> 2 players
> play coins
> tub to use as 'bank'
> coin spinner (ask your teacher for this)

How to play:
> Give the 'bank' 30p in change.
> Start with 70p each made up as follows:
> ten 1p coins   two 10p coins
> five 2p coins   one 20p coin
> two 5p coins

Take turns to spin the spinner. 'Spend' means put the money in the bank. 'Save' means take the money from the bank. 'Give' means give the money to the other player. The winner is the one with more money when the game is stopped.

Half

Colour half.

Draw in the missing half.

Draw a line to cut in half.

 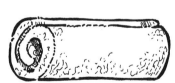  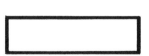

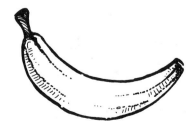  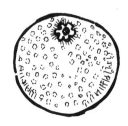

Write how much.

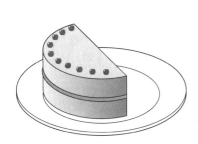

half

$$\frac{1}{2}$$

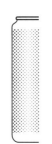 

Draw half of these.

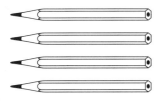

Write the number.	
Half of 2 is	
$\frac{1}{2}$ of 4 is	
6 is half of	
8 is $\frac{1}{2}$ of	
What is half of 10?	

Quarter

Match each quarter to a whole.

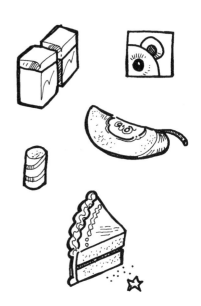

Colour a quarter.

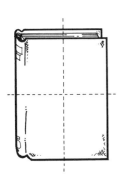
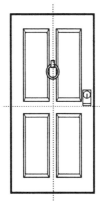
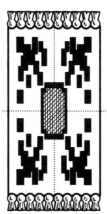
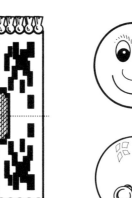

Draw lines to cut into quarters.

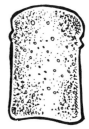

Button box quarters

Draw a circle around a quarter of each set of buttons.

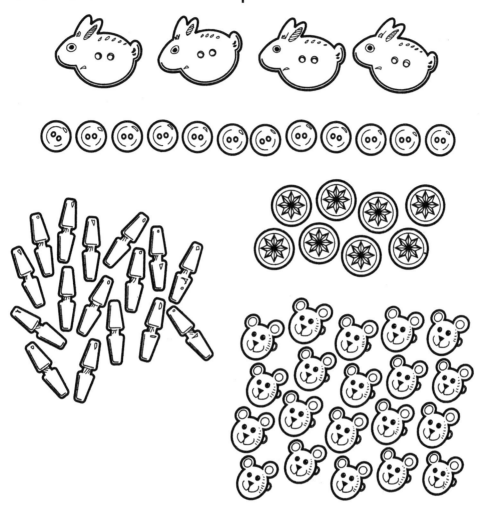

Each set is a quarter. Draw enough buttons for each set to make the whole number.

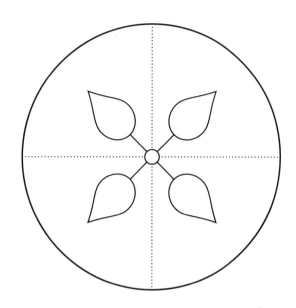

Colour
a quarter red,
a quarter blue and
a quarter black.

How much is left white?

Write the word for $\frac{1}{4}$.

_____   _____   _____

Write what is a quarter of:

8 [ ]   12 [ ]

20 [ ]   16 [ ]

Write in the symbol for a quarter.

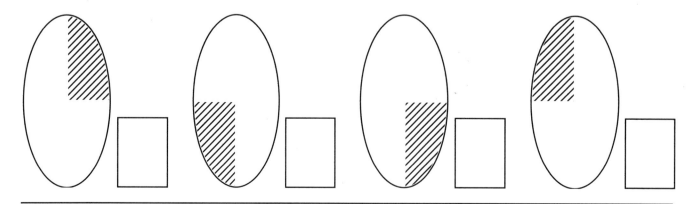

Fractions on a number line

Turn the page sideways. Take care completing the number line.

Put the numbers where they go on the number line, like this:

$4\frac{1}{2}$ $7\frac{3}{4}$ $10\frac{1}{4}$ $13\frac{1}{2}$ $16\frac{3}{4}$

$1\frac{1}{4}$ $5\frac{1}{2}$ $9\frac{1}{2}$ $12\frac{1}{4}$ $17\frac{3}{4}$

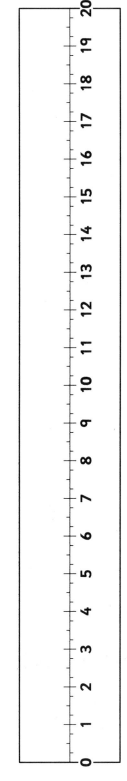

Use the number line to help you do these calculations.

$3\frac{1}{2}$ + $\frac{1}{2}$ = ☐ 17 + $\frac{1}{2}$ = ☐

$7\frac{1}{2}$ + $\frac{1}{2}$ = ☐ $\frac{1}{2}$ + 10 = ☐

$\frac{1}{2}$ + 8 = ☐ 19 + $\frac{1}{2}$ = ☐

11 + $1\frac{1}{2}$ = ☐ 6 + $2\frac{1}{2}$ = ☐

$5\frac{1}{2}$ + 12 = ☐ 7 + ☐ = $13\frac{1}{2}$

$\frac{1}{2}$ + $16\frac{1}{2}$ = ☐   ☐ + 9 = $10\frac{1}{2}$

2 − $\frac{1}{2}$ = ☐ 15 − $4\frac{1}{2}$ = ☐

$5\frac{1}{2}$ − $\frac{1}{2}$ = ☐ $13\frac{1}{2}$ − ☐ = 5

8 + $3\frac{1}{2}$ = ☐ 20 − ☐ = $17\frac{1}{2}$

$12\frac{1}{2}$ − $7\frac{1}{2}$ = ☐   ☐ − $6\frac{1}{2}$ = 11

Write the correct numbers in the boxes.

| 2 | lots of | 2 | make | |

| | lot of | | makes | |

| | lots of | | make | |

| | lots of | | make | |

| | lots of | | make | |

| | lots of | | make | |

| | lots of | | make | |

| | lots of | | make | |

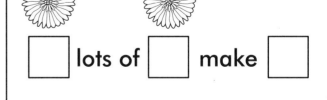

| | lots of | | make | |

| | lots of | | make | |

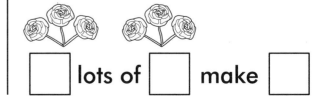

| | lots of | | make | |

Use these beads to help you.

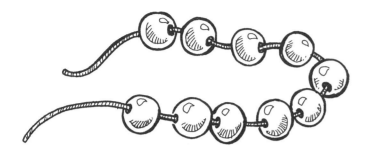

1 lot of 6 makes ☐

2 lots of 3 make ☐

3 lots of 1 make ☐

1 lot of 4 makes ☐   3 lots of 2 make ☐

What is the product?

Use a number line or counting blocks to help if you need to.

1 times 2 ☐   1 lot of 5 ☐

3 times 3 ☐   2 lots of 5 ☐

4 lots of 2 ☐   3 times 2 ☐

$1 \times 2 =$ ☐ $4 \times 2 =$ ☐ $2 \times 4 =$ ☐

$2 \times 2 =$ ☐ $1 \times 3 =$ ☐ $2 \times 3 =$ ☐

---

5 ☐ $1 = 5$ 4×1 ☐ 4

2 ☐ $3 = 6$ 2×0 ☐ 0

3 ☐ $3 = 9$ 10×1 ☐ 10

Multiplication puzzles

Write the missing number in the box.

☐ × 2 = 2   3 × ☐ = 6

☐ × 2 = 10   4 × ☐ = 12

☐ × 2 = 6   5 × ☐ = 10

Put in the numbers to make the multiplications correct.

Make multiplications from these pictures.

Write here.

Write here.

Write here.

Write here.

Multiply game

You need 2 players, 2 counters, a dice marked 1, 2, 2, 3, 3, 4 and a spinner.
Throw the dice to make a move. When you land on a X, throw the dice and spin the spinner. Multiply the scores. Move on your next go.

Start

Finish

Two times table puzzles

Write the products in the two times table rocket.

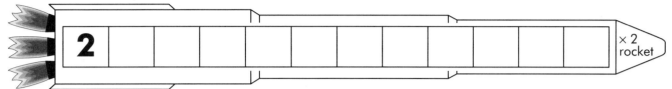

2 ... × 2 rocket

Join up the 2× table products in the right order to complete the moon buggy.

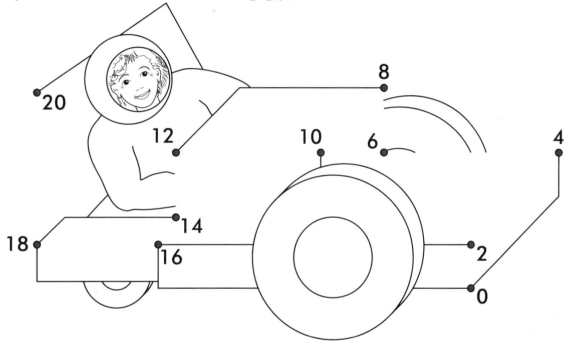

20   12   8   10   6   4   14   18   16   2   0

20

2

0   Rocket countdown

Write the products in this two times table rocket. Start at 20.

Write out the 2× table carefully.

2 × table
1 × 2 = 2

Five times table puzzles

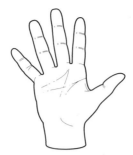

Write the missing number in the box.

☐ = 4 ×   ☐ = 3 ×

☐ = 10 ×   ☐ = 5 ×

Write the missing sign and number in each box.

1 × 5 ☐	4 × 5 ☐	7 × 5 ☐
5 × 1 ☐	5 × 4 ☐	5 × 7 ☐
2 × 5 ☐	5 × 5 ☐	8 × 5 ☐
5 × 2 ☐	6 × 5 ☐	5 × 8 ☐
3 × 5 ☐	5 × 6 ☐	9 × 5 ☐
5 × 3 ☐		5 × 9 ☐

Colour the numbers that are products in the 5 times table.

15	17	35	2	50
3	30	13	20	11
55	27	5	6	10
53	45	14	60	16
25	62	0	41	40

Write out the 5 × table here

0 × 5 = 0

Cut out cards. Mix them up. Match the multiplications to the products.

1 × 5	2 × 5	3 × 5
4 × 5	5 × 5	6 × 5
7 × 5	8 × 5	9 × 5
10 × 5	11 × 5	12 × 5
5	10	15
20	25	30
35	40	45
50	55	60

2×, 5× and 10× table puzzles

$2 \times 2 \times 4 =$ ☐ $10 \times 5 \times 2 =$ ☐

$5 \times 3 \times 2 =$ ☐ $2 \times 6 \times 2 =$ ☐

$2 \times 10 \times 2 =$ ☐ $5 \times 2 \times 2 =$ ☐

Colour the top of the kite if its number is in the 5× table. Colour the bottom in a different colour if the number is in the 10× table. Colour the bow if the number is in the 2× table.

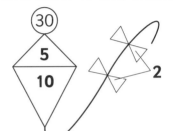
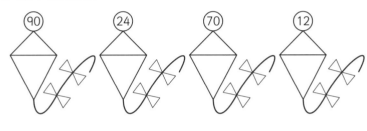

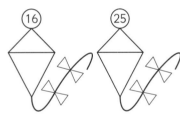
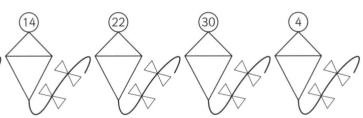

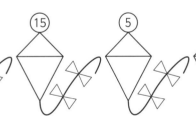
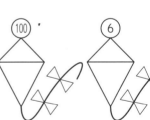
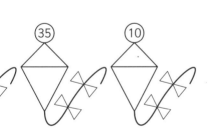

Now write down all three tables.

× 2		× 5		× 10	
1 × 2 = 2					

3× and 4× table puzzles

Write the products of three in the boxes.

× 3

0 × 3 = ☐
1 × 3 = ☐
2 × 3 = ☐
3 × 3 = ☐
4 × 3 = ☐
5 × 3 = ☐

Continue to write the numbers in the fish. Then colour the fish numbers in the pattern of 3s.

× 4

| 0 | 4 | | | | |

Write in the pattern of counting in 4s on the stepping stones.

Write the multiplications to go with these nets.

1 × 4 = 4

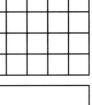

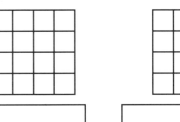

Colour numbers that are products in the 3 × table pink, those in the 4 × table blue.

12

| 3 | 8 | 16 | 6 |

| | 20 | 4 | |

| | 9 | 15 | |

Which number is pink **and** blue? ☐

Multiplication Bingo

Cut out Bingo cards.

5 × 4	3 × 3	0 × 2
0 × 5	4 × 3	1 × 2
1 × 5	5 × 3	3 × 2
2 × 5	0 × 4	4 × 2
3 × 5	1 × 4	5 × 2
4 × 5	2 × 4	0 × 3
5 × 5	3 × 4	1 × 3
2 × 2	4 × 4	2 × 3

Cut out Bingo baseboards.

Choice	0
9	16
25	10
4	15

3	2
8	12
5	20
Choice	6

Multiplication squares

Complete these multiplication squares.

×	**5**	**1**
2		
5		

×	**3**	**4**
2		
5		

×	**2**	☐
☐	**2**	**3**
2	☐	**6**

×	**1**	☐
☐	**5**	☐
3	☐	**0**

Make and complete your own multiplication squares.

×		

×		

15	10	8
20	6	9
4	18	6
12	16	14

Jump along the line and show these divisions.

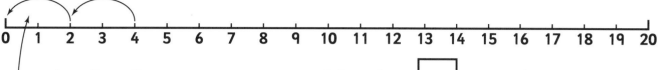

4 ÷ 2 = 2

This division has been
drawn for you.

12 ÷ 2 = ☐

Draw this division on the line
above using a coloured pencil.

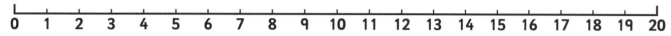

Draw these two divisions on the line above using different colours.

16 ÷ 4 = ☐   **15 ÷ 5 =** ☐

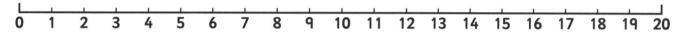

Draw these two divisions on the line above using different colours.

10 ÷ 5 = ☐   **9 ÷ 3 =** ☐

Look carefully at the jumps. Write in the divisions.

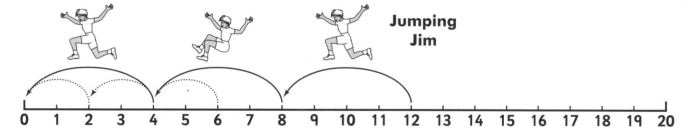

**Jumping
Jim**

········▶ ☐ ÷ ☐ = ☐   ──────▶ ☐ ÷ ☐ = ☐

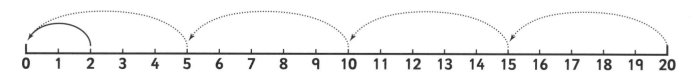

········▶ ☐ ÷ ☐ = ☐   ──────▶ ☐ ÷ ☐ = ☐

Write the missing answers in the boxes.

4 ÷ 2 = ☐

2 ÷ 2 = ☐

18 ÷ 2 = ☐

12 ÷ 2 = ☐

16 ÷ 2 = ☐

See how quickly you can do these

10 ÷ 2 = ☐

14 ÷ 2 = ☐

6 ÷ 2 = ☐

8 ÷ 2 = ☐

20 ÷ 2 = ☐

Divide the numbers in the circle by 2. Match and join each one to its answer.

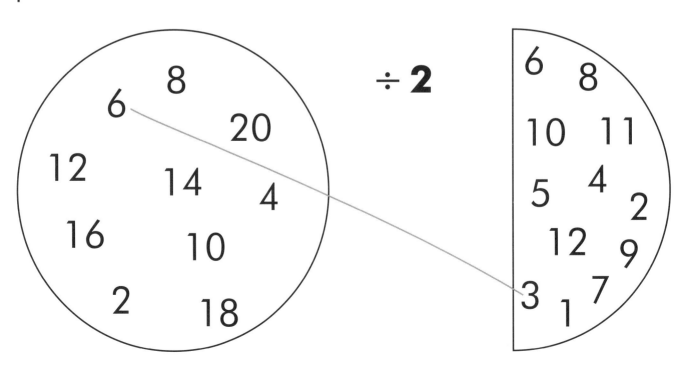

÷ **2**

65 | Divide by 5

Use a number line to help with these.

Divide by 5.

30 ÷ 5 = ☐   10 ÷ 5 = ☐

15 ÷ 5 = ☐   55 ÷ 5 = ☐

60 ÷ 5 = ☐   5 ÷ 5 = ☐

25 ÷ 5 = ☐   45 ÷ 5 = ☐

40 ÷ 5 = ☐   20 ÷ 5 = ☐

50 ÷ 5 = ☐   35 ÷ 5 = ☐

Colour the windows on the skyscrapers in fives using two different colours. Can you see how to make divisions from these patterns?

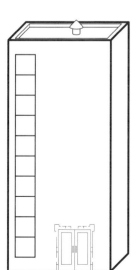
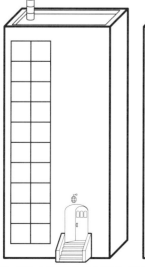

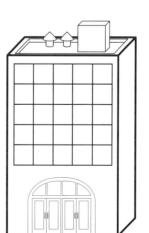
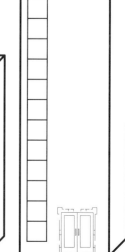

Divide by 2, 5 and 10

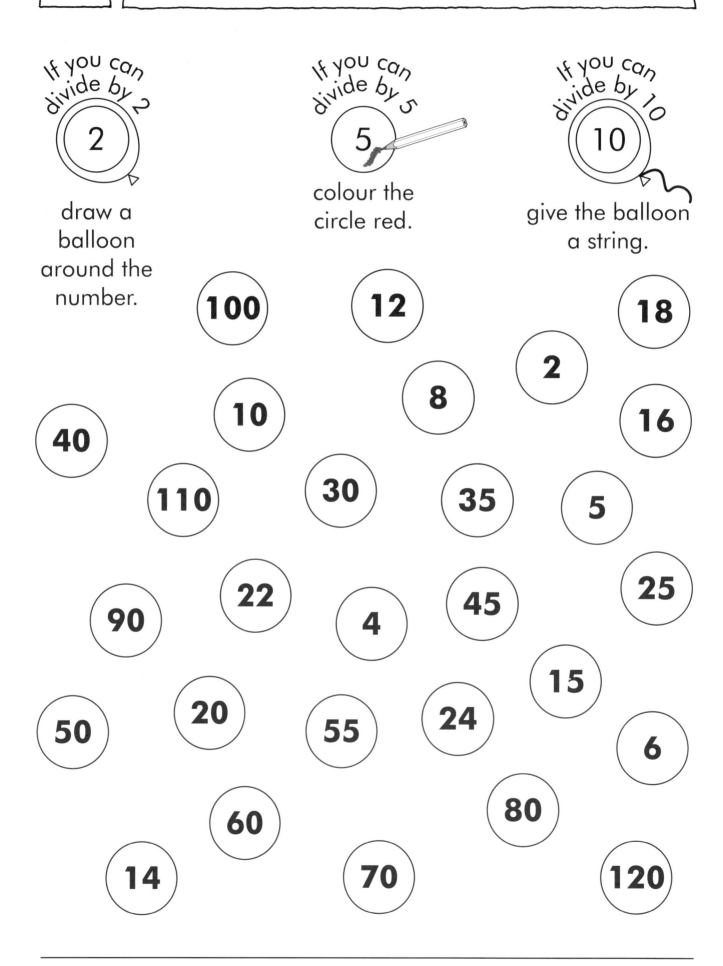

If you can divide by 2

2

draw a balloon around the number.

If you can divide by 5

5

colour the circle red.

If you can divide by 10

10

give the balloon a string.

100

12

18

2

8

16

40

10

110

30

35

5

22

90

45

4

25

15

50

20

55

24

6

60

80

14

70

120

67 | Division game

You need 2 players, 1 dice, 2 pens or pencils of different colours and 2 counters.

Throw the dice to move. If you land on a division square, do the division and then colour the answer circle in your colour here. When one player reaches 100 or beyond, count the circles coloured. The player with the most coloured is the winner.

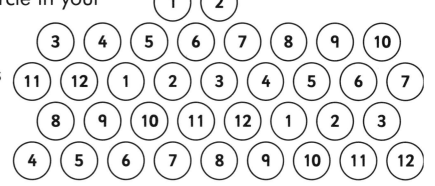

			55÷5			70÷10		24÷2	
100	**99**	**98**	**97**	**96**	**95**	**94**	**93**	**92**	**91**
	100÷10				40÷5		110÷10		40÷10
81	**82**	**83**	**84**	**85**	**86**	**87**	**88**	**89**	**90**
50÷10			8÷2				6÷2		
80	**79**	**78**	**77**	**76**	**75**	**74**	**73**	**72**	**71**
	5÷5		45÷5		10÷5				50÷5
61	**62**	**63**	**64**	**65**	**66**	**67**	**68**	**69**	**70**
60÷10			30÷10		4÷2		25÷5		
60	**59**	**58**	**57**	**56**	**55**	**54**	**53**	**52**	**51**
2÷2		10÷2			20÷10				20÷5
41	**42**	**43**	**44**	**45**	**46**	**47**	**48**	**49**	**50**
90÷10			60÷5			16÷2		18÷2	
40	**39**	**38**	**37**	**36**	**35**	**34**	**33**	**32**	**31**
	14÷2			12÷2		120÷10		30÷5	
21	**22**	**23**	**24**	**25**	**26**	**27**	**28**	**29**	**30**
	15÷5					20÷2			35÷5
20	**19**	**18**	**17**	**16**	**15**	**14**	**13**	**12**	**11**
	80÷10			22÷2			10÷10		
1	**2**	**3**	**4**	**5**	**6**	**7**	**8**	**9**	**10**

Approximate these numbers.

is approximately

11

21

46

9

Share and approximate.

| shared between 2 | shared between 5 | shared between 3 | shared between 10 |

——————————— approximately ———————————

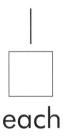 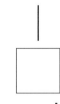 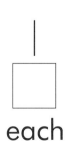

each   each   each   each

Give an approximation for each of these numbers.

9   99    999

Odd and even numbers

Write which numbers are **odd**.

| 1 | 2 | 3 | 4 | 5 | 6 | 7 | 8 | 9 | 10 |

↑
odd

Colour the odd number houses yellow.
Colour the even number houses green.

Patterns in number

Continue the patterns. What comes next?

▭ ● ▭ ● ▭

1 2 3 **1 2 3** **1** ___ ___ ___

0 2 4 6 8 **0 2** ___ ___

8 9 8 9 8 9 ___ ___ ___ ___

5 4 3 2 1 **5 4** ___ ___

3 6 9 **3 6 9** **3** _____

_____

_____

Number bonds by heart

0 + 1 ☐	0 + 6 ☐	5 + 3 ☐	6 + 4 ☐
1 + 0 ☐	1 + 5 ☐	6 + 2 ☐	7 + 3 ☐
0 + 2 ☐	2 + 4 ☐	7 + 1 ☐	8 + 2 ☐
1 + 1 ☐	3 + 3 ☐	8 + 0 ☐	9 + 1 ☐
2 + 0 ☐	4 + 2 ☐	0 + 9 ☐	10 + 0 ☐
0 + 3 ☐	5 + 1 ☐	1 + 8 ☐	
1 + 2 ☐	6 + 0 ☐	2 + 7 ☐	
2 + 1 ☐	0 + 7 ☐	3 + 6 ☐	4 + 4 + 2 ☐
3 + 0 ☐	1 + 6 ☐	4 + 5 ☐	1 + 3 + 1 ☐
0 + 4 ☐	2 + 5 ☐	5 + 4 ☐	7 + 1 + 2 ☐
1 + 3 ☐	3 + 4 ☐	6 + 3 ☐	2 + 2 + 2 ☐
2 + 2 ☐	4 + 3 ☐	7 + 2 ☐	3 + 3 ☐
3 + 1 ☐	5 + 2 ☐	8 + 1 ☐	3 + 3 + 3 ☐
4 + 0 ☐	6 + 1 ☐	9 + 0 ☐	4 + 4 ☐
0 + 5 ☐	7 + 0 ☐	0 + 10 ☐	5 + 5 ☐
1 + 3 ☐	0 + 8 ☐	1 + 9 ☐	0 + 1 + 1 ☐
2 + 3 ☐	1 + 7 ☐	2 + 8 ☐	1 + 2 + 3 ☐
3 + 2 ☐	2 + 6 ☐	3 + 7 ☐	4 + 2 + 2 ☐
4 + 1 ☐	3 + 5 ☐	4 + 6 ☐	2 + 3 + 4 ☐
5 + 0 ☐	4 + 4 ☐	5 + 5 ☐	1 + 3 + 5 ☐

Work fast. Easy cheesy.

Doubling and halving

Write the 'doubles' in the boxes.

1 doubled is ☐   6 ☐

2 ☐   7 ☐

3 ☐   8 ☐

4 ☐   9 ☐

5 ☐   10 ☐

Write the 'halves' in the boxes.

8 halved is ☐   16 ☐

12 ☐   30 ☐

24 ☐   28 ☐

8 ☐   26 ☐

What are the doubles here?

30 ☐   50 ☐

10 ☐   25 ☐

15 ☐   5 ☐

20 ☐   40 ☐

Doubling and halving is easy to do. Just think carefully.

Missing number game

You need 2 players, 1 dice and 2 counters. Take turns to throw the dice and move your counter on the board. Choose a wall each, and when you land on a calculation square, find the missing number. If the number is in your wall cross it out. The winner is the player with all or most bricks crossed out.

FINISH		$6 \div \square = 2$		$16 + \square = 66$	$20 \div \square = 10$
36	35	34	33	32	31
$3 \times \square = 30$	$\square \times 3 \times 2 = 18$	$\square \times 3 = 15$		$26 - \square = 19$	$41 + \square = 45$
25	26	27	28	29	30
$25 + \square = 41$	$25 \div \square = 5$		$17 + \square = 23$	$9 + \square = 13$	
24	23	22	21	20	19
$16 \div \square = 8$		$\square + 8 = 15$	$18 \div \square = 6$	$70 + \square = 86$	$50 - \square = 35$
13	14	15	16	17	18
	$\square + 30 = 45$	$20 + \square = 70$	$50 \div 10 = \square$	$\square \times 1 \times 3 = 9$	$5 \times \square = 50$
12	11	10	9	8	7
START		$16 - \square = 12$		$8 \times \square = 40$	
1	2	3	4	5	6

Function machine calculations

Write in the inputs to Rudy the Robot.

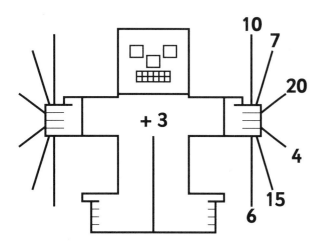

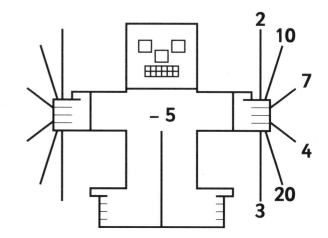

Write in the outputs.

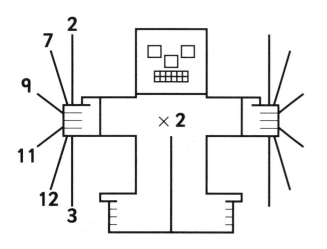

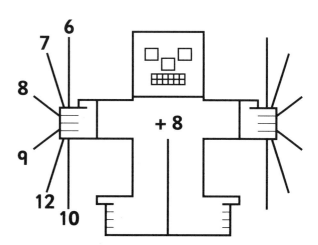

Write in what these function machines are doing.

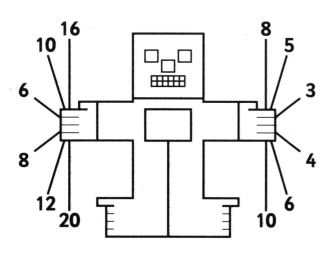

Writing prices

Write these prices in numbers.

ninety-nine pence

forty-five pence

one pound twenty

How many pounds here?

£3.56

£22.49

How many pence in these prices?

 £2.60

 £5.99

£1.30

Write these prices in numbers.

Fifteen pounds eleven

Sixty pounds ten

Sixteen pounds thirty

Eight pounds eighty-seven

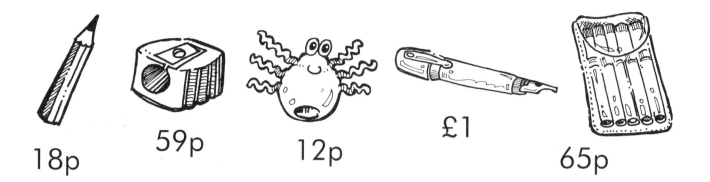

76 | Going shopping

18p 59p 12p £1 65p

Go shopping. Write how much these cost.

+ cost

+ + cost

+ cost

+ + cost

What do these cost?

2 pens

4 pencils

5 pencil tops

a sharpener and a pen

felt tips and a pencil

Giving change

I give:	I spend:	My change: (draw around coins)

Shopping game

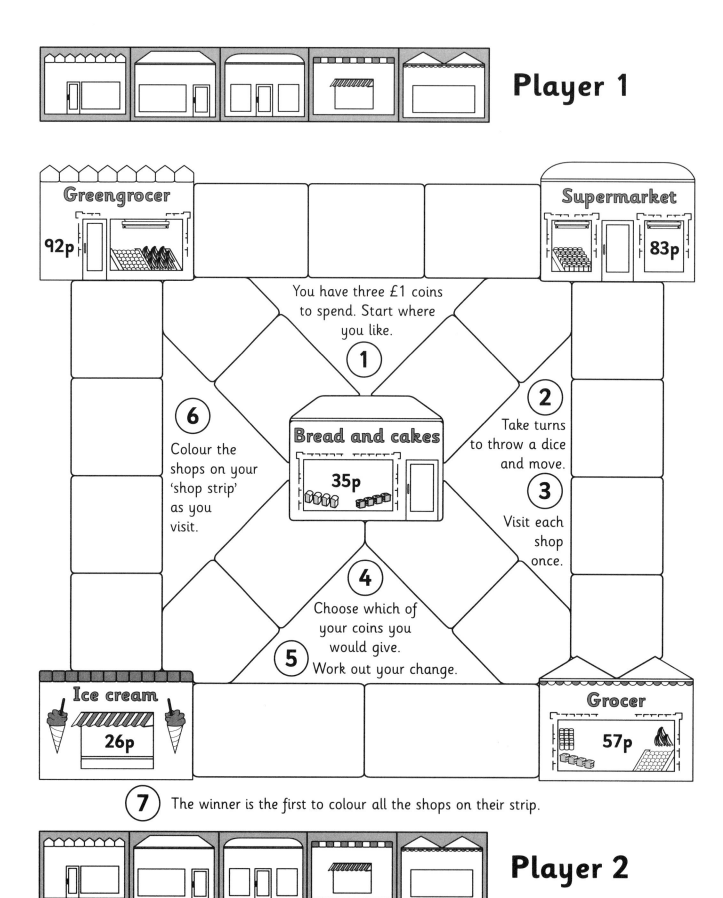

Player 1

Greengrocer 92p

Supermarket 83p

You have three £1 coins to spend. Start where you like.

(1)

(2) Take turns to throw a dice and move.

(3) Visit each shop once.

(6) Colour the shops on your 'shop strip' as you visit.

Bread and cakes 35p

(4) Choose which of your coins you would give.

(5) Work out your change.

Ice cream 26p

Grocer 57p

(7) The winner is the first to colour all the shops on their strip.

Player 2

Try doing these in your head. Remember to change the order of the numbers where it makes the calculation easier.

$14 + 6 =$ ☐

$27 + 1 =$ ☐

$40 - 20 =$ ☐

$8 + 31 =$ ☐

$19 - 6 =$ ☐

$9 + 72 =$ ☐

$35 - 9 =$ ☐

$5 + 15 + 5 =$ ☐

$17 - 11 =$ ☐

$0 + 90 + 1 =$ ☐

$2 \times 5 =$ ☐

$2 \times 15 =$ ☐

$3 \times 6 =$ ☐

$9 \times 2 =$ ☐

$30 \div 10 =$ ☐

$60 \div 5 =$ ☐

Sorting

Sort and draw these in the two sets below.

Sort and draw these in the three sets below.

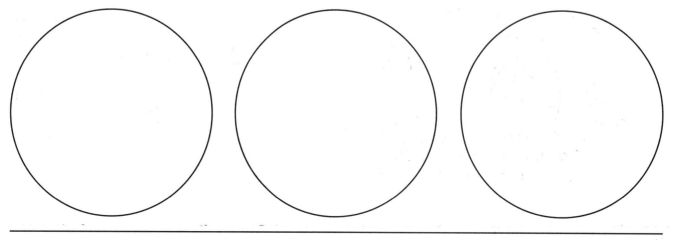

Join up. Give each balloon man 5 balloons.

Give each dog a bone.

Give each drink a straw.   Send each bee to a flower.

Dogs and cats in my workgroup.

Some children are playing with a bat and a ball.
Colour one bat below for each child you see
playing with one in the picture.

How many children are
playing bat and ball in total?

Carroll diagrams

Put these pictures into the Carroll diagrams

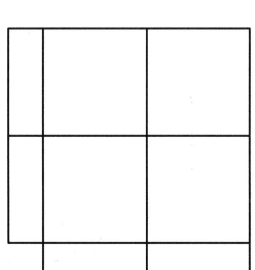

Weather chart

Here is a chart showing the weather for 4 weeks.

Sunday	☀	☁	☀	☀
Monday	☁	☂	☀	☀
Tuesday	☀	☀	☀	☀
Wednesday	☂	☂	☂	☂
Thursday	☂	☂	☀	☀
Friday	☁	☁	☂	☂
Saturday	☁	☁	☁	☁

Which day was sunny every week? _____

Which day was rainy every week? _____

Which day was cloudy every week? _____

Which day was best for playing out? _____

Which day was best for playing indoors? _____

Library books

This chart shows how often books about these subjects were borrowed in a month.

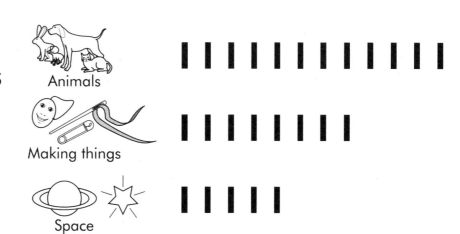

Animals | | | | | | | | | | | | |

Making things | | | | | | | |

Space | | | | |

Which books were borrowed least? _____

Which books are most popular? _____

Which books were borrowed eight times? _____

How many times were animal books borrowed? _____

Picture cards: count to 5

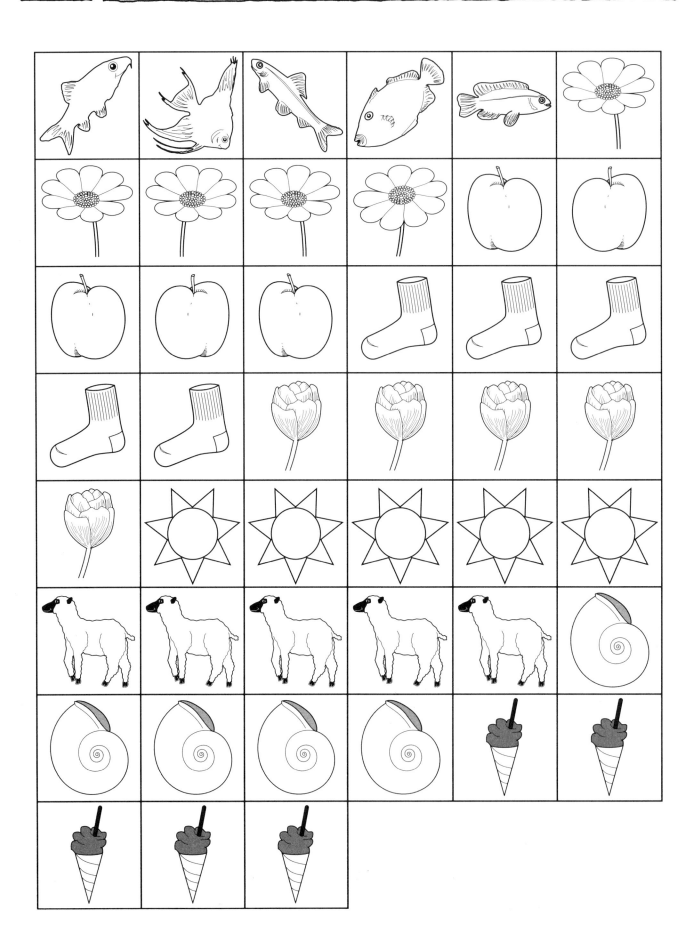

Hundred square

1	2	3	4	5	6	7	8	9	10
11	12	13	14	15	16	17	18	19	20
21	22	23	24	25	26	27	28	29	30
31	32	33	34	35	36	37	38	39	40
41	42	43	44	45	46	47	48	49	50
51	52	53	54	55	56	57	58	59	60
61	62	63	64	65	66	67	68	69	70
71	72	73	74	75	76	77	78	79	80
81	82	83	84	85	86	87	88	89	90
91	92	93	94	95	96	97	98	99	100

Round and round the garden

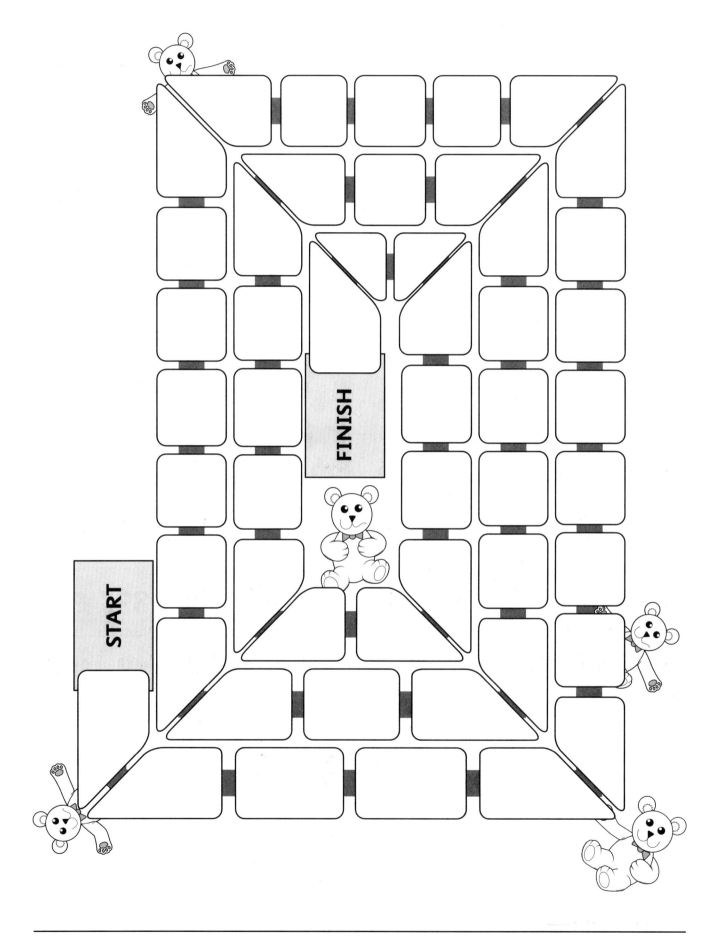

Shopping mall game

100	99	98	97	96	95 going down	94	93	92	91
81	**82**	83	84	85	86	87	88	89	**90**
80	79 going up	78	**77**	76	75	74	73	72	71
61	62 going down	63	64	65	**66**	67	68	69 going down	70
60	59	**58**	57	56	55 going up	54	**53**	52	51 going up
41	42	43	**44**	45	46	**47**	48	**49**	50
40	**39**	38	37	36	35	34	33	32	31
21	22	23	24	25 going down	26	27	28	29	30
20	19	18	17	16	15	14	13	12 going up	11
1 Start	2 going up	3	4	5	6	7	8	9	10

Spinners

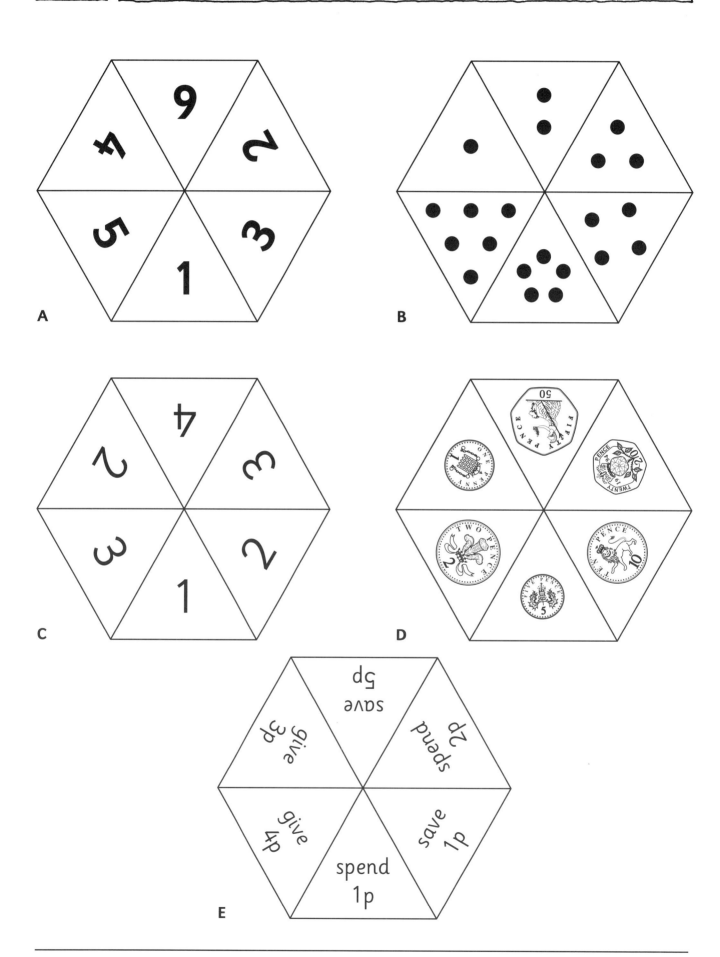

			0	19	20
$1\frac{1}{2}$	$1\frac{3}{4}$	$\frac{1}{2}$	$\frac{1}{4}$	$\frac{3}{4}$	$2\frac{1}{4}$
$1\frac{1}{4}$	$2\frac{1}{2}$	$2\frac{3}{4}$	$3\frac{1}{4}$	$3\frac{1}{2}$	$3\frac{3}{4}$
$4\frac{1}{4}$	$4\frac{1}{2}$	$4\frac{3}{4}$	$5\frac{1}{4}$	$5\frac{1}{2}$	$5\frac{3}{4}$
$6\frac{1}{4}$	$6\frac{1}{2}$	$6\frac{3}{4}$	$7\frac{1}{4}$	$7\frac{1}{2}$	$7\frac{3}{4}$
$8\frac{1}{4}$	$8\frac{1}{2}$	$8\frac{3}{4}$	$9\frac{1}{4}$	$9\frac{1}{2}$	$9\frac{3}{4}$
$10\frac{1}{4}$	$10\frac{1}{2}$	$10\frac{3}{4}$	$11\frac{1}{4}$	$11\frac{1}{2}$	$11\frac{3}{4}$
$12\frac{1}{4}$	$12\frac{1}{2}$	$12\frac{3}{4}$	$13\frac{1}{4}$	$13\frac{1}{2}$	$13\frac{3}{4}$
$14\frac{1}{4}$	$14\frac{1}{2}$	$14\frac{3}{4}$	$15\frac{1}{4}$	$15\frac{1}{2}$	$15\frac{3}{4}$
$16\frac{1}{4}$	$16\frac{1}{2}$	$16\frac{3}{4}$	$17\frac{1}{4}$	$17\frac{1}{2}$	$17\frac{3}{4}$
$18\frac{1}{4}$	$18\frac{1}{2}$	$18\frac{3}{4}$	$19\frac{1}{4}$	$19\frac{1}{2}$	$19\frac{3}{4}$
1	2	3	4	5	6
7	8	9	10	11	12
13	14	15	16	17	18

Number lines

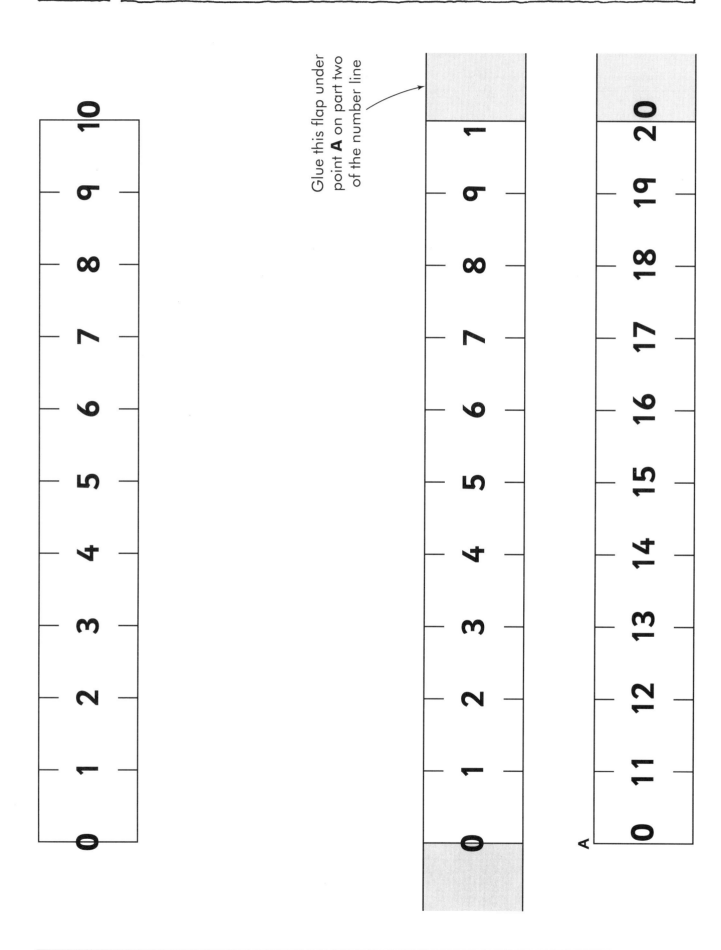

Glue this flap under point **A** on part two of the number line

Half-centimetre squared paper

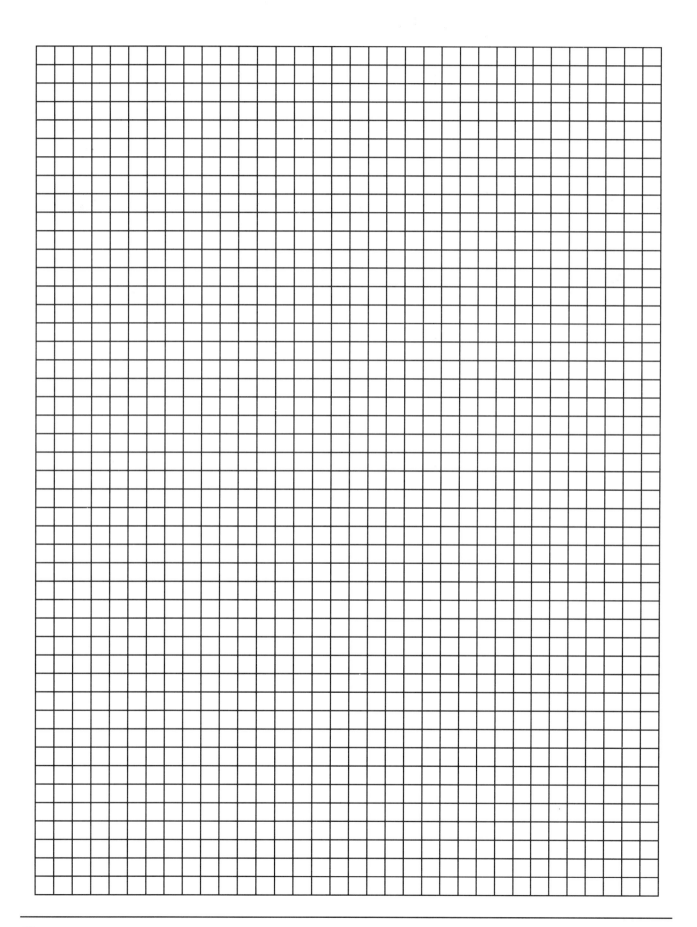

Glue this flap under point **A** on
the next part of the number line

1	20	30	40	50
9	19	29	39	49
8	18	28	38	48
7	17	27	37	47
6	16	26	36	46
5	15	25	35	45
4	14	24	34	44
3	13	23	33	43
2	12	22	32	42
1	11	21	31	41
0	0	0	0	0
	A	A	A	A

Pictures for sorting

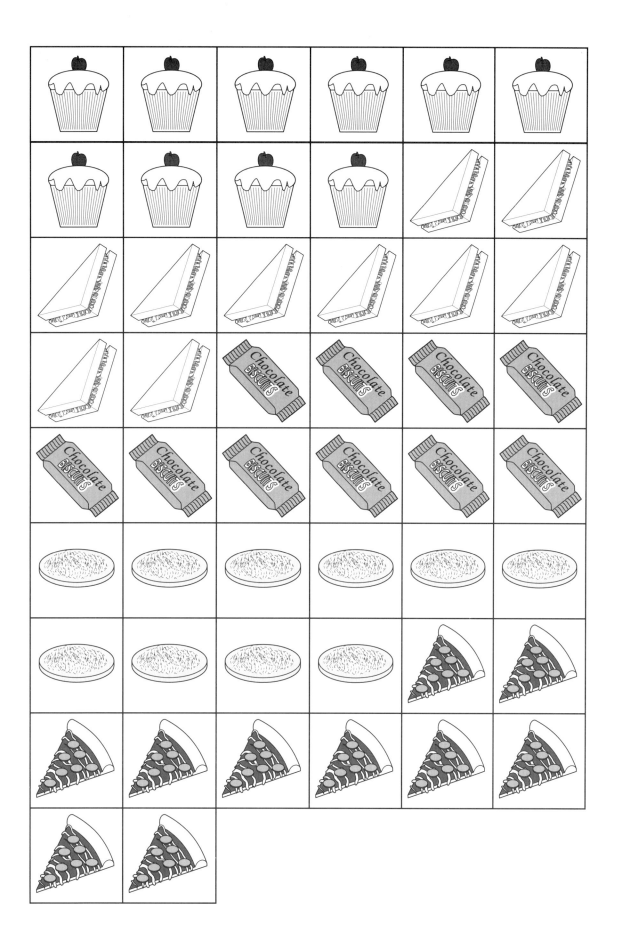

Learning Targets: Number Key Stage 1
RECORD SHEET

Name _____ Class/Year _____ Teacher's initials _____

Section	Theme	Performance in relation to learning targets			Summative remarks
		1	2	3	
Counting	1 Beginning counting				
	2 Reading and writing numbers to 10				
	3 Reading and writing numbers to 20				
	4 All about ordinal number				
	5 Introducing place value				
	6 Working with numbers beyond 99				
Addition and Subtraction	7 Introducing addition				
	8 Adding to 10				
	9 Introducing subtraction				
	10 Subtracting to 10				
	11 Adding and subtracting to 20				
	12 Adding and subtracting to 100				
	13 Adding and subtracting money				
Fractions	14 Half				
	15 Quarter				
	16 The number line				
Multiplication and Division	17 Introducing multiplication				
	18 2, 5 and 10 times tables				
	19 Multiplications up to 5 × 5				
	20 Introducing division				
	21 Dividing by 2, 5 and 10				
	22 Remainders				
Mental Arithmetic and Number Patterns	23 Looking for patterns				
	24 Add, subtract, double and halve to 20				
	25 Missing numbers/function machines/number trails				
	26 Money problems				
	27 Calculation strategies				
Number Data	28 Number pictures				
	29 Charts and graphs				